Understanding Data

Peter Sprent was Professor of Statistics at the University of Dundee from 1972 to 1985. He is now a full-time writer and consultant.

Born in Tasmania in 1923 he lectured at the university there for ten years. He came to the United Kingdom in 1958 and worked as a statistician at East Malling Research Station in Kent before moving to Dundee. He has always had a keen interest in practical statistics and data analysis, having been a consultant in fields ranging from agriculture and biology to industry and commerce.

He is author of *Statistics in Action* and *Quick Statistics*, both published by Penguin, as well as of a research monograph and numerous papers in professional journals. Peter Sprent is a Fellow of The Royal Society of Edinburgh and a member of the International Statistical Institute and other professional bodies.

His hobbies include hill-walking, golf and flying.

ADVISORY EDITORS: Stephen Coote and Bryan Loughrey

Understanding Data

Peter Sprent

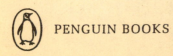

PENGUIN BOOKS

PENGUIN BOOKS

Published by the Penguin Group
27 Wrights Lane, London W8 5TZ, England
Viking Penguin Inc., 40 West 23rd Street, New York, New York 10010, USA
Penguin Books Australia Ltd, Ringwood, Victoria, Australia
Penguin Books Canada Ltd, 2801 John Street, Markham, Ontario, Canada L3R 1B4
Penguin Books (NZ) Ltd, 182–190 Wairau Road, Auckland 10, New Zealand

Penguin Books Ltd, Registered Offices: Harmondsworth, Middlesex, England

First published 1988

Typeset, printed and bound in Great Britain by
Hazell Watson and Viney Limited,
Member of the BPCC Group
Aylesbury, Bucks

Typeset in Linotron 202 Melior

Contents

6

Appendices:

Preface

'Be *literate*', 'Be *numerate*', are popular catchphrases in our sophisticated 'high-tech' society. We must be both if we are to be able to receive and to pass on information, for this can only be done by a sensible blend of words, numbers, pictures and diagrams.

Sadly, some who would be offended if one suggested they were illiterate take pride in claiming to be not numerate. 'I've no head for figures,' their all too familiar apology, adding that mathematics is a frightening mystery, a subject for which they have no skills.

Being numerate has little to do with such skills. It needs only an ability to know when elementary operations like addition, subtraction, multiplication, division or taking a square root are appropriate, and to interpret the results of such operations. Even the mechanics of these operations may usually be left to a pocket calculator or a computer.

One may be literate without being a linguistic scholar, needing to know only the rudiments of grammar; so one may be numerate without studying much mathematics. Even some high-level arithmetic is as little relevant to numeracy as are many obscure grammatical niceties to literacy.

Words alone may suffice for the transmission of qualitative ideas, but quantitative information can only be conveyed by numbers and words together, often supplemented by pictures or diagrams.

This book is about the simplest aspects of understanding and handling data. As a primer it is not a formal textbook or compendium of rules. I make my points by discussing data in a number of contexts. Much of what I say is just common sense, but it is surprising how often the obvious is ignored. This is certainly not a book on the science of statistics, although a few statistical ideas important to data collection and presentation are discussed informally in the later chapters. Nor is it a handbook on using computers or calculators; it concentrates on the fundamentals of data handling.

At all stages I encourage readers to try things for themselves with exercises incorporated in the body of the text. Very often the results of these are used immediately for further developments, so, for a proper understanding it is essential that these exercises – some short and simple, others long and tedious – be attempted. Tackling the exercises will build up confidence, but I have provided a life-line for those in difficulty. Solutions to the more important or exacting exercises, especially ones that introduce new concepts that are not dealt with in the text immediately following the exercise, are discussed in Chapter 21.

Some of the data comes from official sources and these are fully acknowledged at appropriate points in the text. I am particularly grateful to Her Majesty's Stationery Office for permission to use several extracts from records in the Meteorological Office Monthly Weather Reports for 1978 and also data extracted from the *Monthly Digest of Statistics* compiled by the UK Central Statistical Office.

Penguin Books' Mathematics Advisory Editor, David Nelson, as always, came up with many worthwhile suggestions when confronted with the draft manuscript.

Now a plea; we all meet numbers in different contexts. If I give examples well away from your particular field of interest try and think of some analogous situation in your work or from your hobbies. You will be surprised how often there is one.

P. S.

1 Numbers and Tables

1 Collecting data

An old practice

Collecting and processing data has a long history. In the Roman Empire every man had to appear at regular intervals before the magistrates or *censors* (whence our word *census*) and give his name and age, those of his wife, and state how many children and slaves he had; he was questioned too about his wealth.

The purpose was to find how many men there were to bear arms and to provide information for the levying of taxes. It explains why Christ was born in Bethlehem, for 'All went to be taxed, every one into his own city' (Luke II, 3).

A less systematic head count took place in ancient China. It is only in very primitive societies that counts and numbers play no important role; that is one reason they remain primitive. Data collection and analysis meant nothing to the now extinct Tasmanian aborigines. Their entire number system was *one, two, plenty*. Only if we live very simple lives can we manage with so restricted a system.

William the Conqueror carried out an elaborate exercise in collecting information. The results are summarized in the Domesday Book.

Modern developments

The last two centuries have witnessed a data explosion. Just over 200 years ago the United States held its first census, more formal than its Roman forerunner and with wider implications; one aim being to use the data for social planning. The first regular enumeration of UK residents was in 1801. Unsophisticated compared to today's censuses, it aimed to determine the total population, the numbers of inhabited and uninhabited houses, how many people lived in each parish (these being the most important local groupings of that era) and to indicate numbers in broad employment categories – agriculture, trade, manufacturing and handicrafts. It failed in this last aim.

Official data collection, by census or other means, is now just the tip of an iceberg so far as numerical information is concerned. Schools keep details of pupil performance; hospitals record blood pressure, blood chemistry, temperature and diet for each patient; businesses keep files on employees' pay and productivity; the Meteorological Office logs weather data at hundreds of stations; industries and government departments compile records of production for thousands of items, as well as data on imports, exports, employment, transport, accidents, etc. Research workers are for ever collecting data. Each month the UK Government Central Statistical Office publishes a *Monthly Digest of Statistics*; just one of many official statistical publications. A glance at a copy gives some idea of the scope of official statistics alone.

The data explosion has been fuelled by the computer and other mechanical and electronic aids that make it not only ever easier to collect and store data, but also help the processing, which will hopefully elucidate messages lurking behind the figures. Sadly much of this effort is inefficient or misplaced.

Some key questions

Good data collection and processing demands prior thought. Right at the outset ask yourself questions like these:
1. What data do I need?
2. If a set of data is obtained by asking questions: (a) what information is each question seeking and (b) how are the questions best put to avoid bias?
3. How do I make collection, storage and processing cost-

effective? (We use *cost-effective* in a broad sense to cover quick economic collection of adequate data, economical storage, avoidance of irrelevant material, presentation in an easily understood format – indeed, any factor that reduces cost while maintaining, or even enhancing, efficiency.)

4. Given all relevant data, how do I process it to best answer questions of interest?
5. What messages are in a specific data set?
6. How do I present conclusions in easily digestible form?
7. Are my conclusions valid and are there any caveats or special circumstances I should emphasize so that others will not misinterpret or misuse my data or conclusions?

We follow the logic of Lewis Carroll (himself an able mathematician and data explorer) and *begin at the beginning* by discussing data collection.

Data collection

Some people collect data as squirrels do nuts – to put *it* by for a rainy day. I refer to data as *it* knowing full well that strictly *data* is the plural of *datum*. The data explosion has meant that most of us think of data as 'a collection or set composed of datum' and so treat it as a collective noun. At the risk of offending those manning the last bastions of grammatical conservatism I am going to use such phrases as 'this data is'. Purists may translate to 'these data are'. For a more detailed discussion of this point see Moore (1980, p. 192).

As with the squirrels, the data collector's rainy day may never come; painstakingly collected figures lie forgotten in the obscurity of a filing cabinet or are eventually consigned to a bonfire. More often a use is found. A business executive, civil servant, union official, production manager or research worker has a flash of inspiration. Available data may answer a pressing question, uncover past mistakes or point the way to wise decisions about the future; it may highlight a dramatic trend, or a startling change in fortune.

It may, but will it? Unless the data has been collected with a clear aim and is processed accordingly it can fail dismally, or at best be only partially successful.

From the collection point onward *never* forget the aim of the exercise. What might be good data for one purpose may be wholly inadequate for another. Producing a railway timetable is very different from writing a report on computer breakdown patterns – their only common feature is that they both involve numbers! We want different basic information for each task.

Bias

The second key question on p. 10 mentioned the importance of seeking the relevant information in a way that avoided bias. To illustrate this, consider possible ways of finding people's views as to whether Margaret Thatcher is the best post-war Prime Minister. Three ways of framing a question would be:

1. Mrs Thatcher is the best post-war PM   Agree ☐
                                                               Disagree ☐
2. Mrs Thatcher is not the best post-war PM   Agree ☐
                                                               Disagree ☐
3. Circle the name of the best post-war PM:

    Attlee   Churchill   Eden   Macmillan
    Douglas-Home   Wilson   Heath
    Callaghan   Thatcher

The third form has the least danger of bias. Respondents have before them a list of all post-war Prime Ministers in chronological order of appointment and will presumably weigh each one's claim against that of Thatcher. In the first form people who consider Mrs Thatcher is generally doing a good job might well tick the 'agree' box without giving much thought to the claims of the other candidates simply because Mrs Thatcher's name is the only one specifically in front of them. Indeed, they might even have forgotten that Churchill, for instance, was a post-war Prime Minister! The second form is confusing because of the double negative. One has to vote *disagree* if one thinks she is best; it also raises similar objections to the first form.

Not only does the third form avoid bias; it also gives us additional information with little additional effort. It enables us to find out which PM the majority of those interviewed consider best, and whether there is a widely accepted popular choice. A minor criticism of the third form is that the chronological order automatically puts Attlee first and Thatcher last. This objection could be overcome (at additional cost) by preparing questionnaires with the PMs listed in different orders on each but this is probably an unnecessary refinement.

Example 1.1. Computers have made a dramatic contribution to the data explosion, helping in both collection and analysis, but they have their own drawbacks; one of these (we will mention others on pp. 53 and 152) is that they break down. A good manager of a computer installation will keep a record of the duration of each breakdown.

Why? Possible reasons are:

1. He is interested in trends or patterns. Are breakdowns becoming more or less frequent as the machine gets older? Do major breakdowns tend to occur more frequently on, say, Monday mornings; or on the night shift? Are breakdowns more common on peripheral equipment (tape readers, printers, VDUs, disc drives, etc.) than in the central processing unit (the CPU)?

2. Contractual arrangements with the machine supplier or an insurer may provide compensation if average *downtime* (computer jargon for the time the machine is out of use) due to component failures exceeds a certain number of hours in any month, or if one component fails more than a certain number of times per annum.

3. He may wish to compare the breakdown rate for his machine with that of similar ones, or with alternative equipment offered by another supplier.

Table 1.1 is a simple record of breakdown times for one month. It tells us nothing about the frequency and nature of various types of breakdown or about remedial actions. Clearly from it alone we cannot deduce whether a fault is in the computer's CPU or a peripheral. We do not know which faults were repaired by the computer operating staff, or which needed a maintenance engineer.

Table 1.1.   *A company record of computer downtime in minutes, May 1984*

49	18	123	3	87	21	7	24	11	19	243	38
11	18	32	101	6	32	27	41	3	25	19	242
122	15	7	6	2	18	42	24	7	9	14	10
30	23	141	7	102	83	29	11	15	7	6	8
121	4	23	42	18	31	25	42	6	339	19	27
12	11	3	5	9	3	22	17	20	5	3	18
142	51	18	41	9	9	27	14	33	128	34	18
232	179	143	181	6	14						

Exercise 1.1.   What percentage of downtimes in May 1984 exceeded one hour? Try and get the answer before reading on.

Table 1.1 has the answer hidden away. A simple count shows 17 of the 90 breakdowns lasted over an hour. The percentage is got by multiplying the proportion 17/90 by 100, giving 18.89% if we round to 2 decimal places. This amount of rounding is a somewhat arbitrary decision and after reading p. 20 you may decide it is not a very sensible one!

In Chapter 3 we look in more detail at uses of data like that in Table 1.1.

Example 1.2.   Table 1.2 looks long and complex. At this stage I am not asking you to study it in great detail. It enables us to answer many questions about when and where breakdowns occurred, a range much wider than is possible with Table 1.1. If you find it perplexing don't give up hope. One of the aims of this book is to show how we may cope more easily with such data by rearranging it. In later chapters we shall often refer back to Table 1.2. To save repeated flicking back it might be worth your while to prepare copies of it (photocopies would do nicely) to have beside you when needed. Copies of Table 1.1 and 1.3 would also be useful.

Table 1.2. *Record of computer breakdowns, May 1984*

Day	Time of breakdown	Equipment	Duration (mins)	Day	Time of breakdown	Equipment	Duration (mins)
Tu 1	0842	Printer	49		1451	Printer	18
We 2	1035	Disc drive	18		1516	Printer	42
	1529	CPU	123	Mo 14	1759	Disc drive	24
	1735	CPU	3	Tu 15	0803	Printer	7
Th 3					0817	Printer	9
Fr 4	1109	Tape reader	87		0831	Printer	14
	1907	Printer	21		0847	Printer	10
	2033	Printer	7		0905	Printer	30
	2051	Printer	24		0942	Printer	23
Sa 5	0835	Printer	11		1009	Printer	141
	0922	Printer	19		1240	Printer	7
Su 6	0900	Service	243		1249	Printer	102
Mo 7	1525	Graph plotter	38		1947	CPU	83
Tu 8	0947	CPU	11	We 16	1429	Graph plotter	29
	1010	CPU	18	Th 17			
We 9	1432	Disc drive	32	Fr 18			
	1527	CPU	101	Sa 19	1033	Disc drive	11
	1712	CPU	6		1102	Disc drive	15
	1809	Tape reader	32		1221	Disc drive	7
	1931	Printer	27		1234	Disc drive	6
	2122	CPU	41		1247	Disc drive	8
Th 10	0805	Printer	3		1342	Disc drive	121
Fr 11	1331	Printer	25		1829	Graph plotter	4
	1447	Printer	19	Su 20	1328	Tape reader	23
	1702	Tape reader	242		1700	Graph plotter	42
Sa 12					1748	Graph plotter	18
Su 13	1022	CPU	122	Mo 21	0904	Tape reader	31
	1403	Printer	15		1227	Disc drive	25
	1422	Printer	7		1513	Printer	42
	1433	Printer	6		1907	Printer	6
	1445	Printer	2	Tu 22	0800	Service	339

Day	Time of break-down	Equipment	Dura-tion (mins)	Day	Time of break-down	Equipment	Dura-tion (mins)
	1926	Disc drive	19		1707	Disc drive	18
	2240	Graph plotter	27		1729	Disc drive	41
We 23	0931	Tape reader	12		1944	Printer	9
	0952	Tape reader	11	Mo 28	1137	Graph plotter	9
	1005	Tape reader	3		1430	Tape reader	27
	1017	Tape reader	5		1504	Tape reader	14
	1024	Tape reader	9	Tu 29	0913	Graph plotter	33
	1038	Tape reader	3		0952	CPU	128
	1402	CPU	22		1244	CPU	34
	1823	CPU	17		1359	Tape reader	18
Th 24					1505	CPU	232
Fr 25	2129	Graph plotter	20		1901	CPU	179
Sa 26	1340	Tape reader	5		2206	CPU	143
	1545	Tape reader	3	We 30	0801	CPU	181
	1550	Tape reader	18		1212	Printer	6
Su 27	0955	CPU	142	Th 31	2105	Tape reader	14
	1235	CPU	51				

Exercise 1.2. Compare the entries in the last column of Table 1.2 with those in Table 1.1. What do you notice?

The numbers are the same, implying that the tables refer to the same incidents. Column 3 tells us if the downtime is for routine servicing or if it is due to a breakdown in the CPU or any named peripheral. It is not *numerical* in the sense of consisting of numbers, but it provides a basis for *classification*, an important facet of data collection and interpretation.

In Chapter 4 we look at ways of putting the data in Table 1.2 in more useful forms for specific purposes. Clearly it provides a wealth of information not in Table 1.1. A quick glance indicates, for example, that May 4, 9, 13, 15, 19, 21, 23, 27, 29 were all days with four or more breakdowns. We notice 'runs' of trouble with certain components; May 13 and 15 were bad days for the printer; the disc drive proved troublesome on May 19; the CPU gave serious trouble on the 29th and 30th.

Exercise 1.3.   Look at Table 1.2. Can you spot any bad spells for the tape reader or the graph plotter? With what types of event are the two longest downtimes associated?

There are hints and discussion of this and many other exercises in Chapter 21.

Column 2 may seem of less immediate interest than column 3 but it is useful for answering questions about the spread of breakdowns throughout the working day (assumed to be from 0800 to 2400 hours daily); see Exercise 4.6 on p. 53.

How much information?

Information we record should be governed by what is, or is likely to be, of interest. We might want even more information than that in Table 1.2. For example, some peripheral breakdowns do not result in a shut-down of the whole system; the rest may still be usable while these peripherals are out of action. From the operational point of view it may be desirable to know for each breakdown whether it resulted in a shut-down of the whole system, or only the portion (printer, reader, etc.) actually malfunctioning. We could either log (i.e. record) separately complete and partial shut-downs, or add a column to Table 1.2 indicating whether each shut-down was complete or partial (using the letters C, P). We might also want to know which faults were dealt with by operating staff and which needed engineers. With hindsight one often regrets not recording certain information or alternatively feels that some that has been collected is of little use; so we must think seriously about what data to collect in any given situation. We won't always get it 100 per cent right, but it may save us collecting useless data, or, what is more frustrating, failing to collect all we really need.

For each breakdown the appropriate entry in Table 1.2 takes less than a minute to record; the additional items make it more useful than Table 1.1.

'Raw' data of this type, particularly if there is much of it, is hard to digest unless we *process* or *summarize* it. Suppose we had not just data on computer breakdowns for one month but for a whole year; if the total of ninety breakdowns for May is typical we may well then have information on a thousand or more breakdowns each year; records occupying many pages. In a format like Table 1.2 extracting specific information would take a long time. We tackle this type of problem in Chapter 4.

Accuracy and precision

If *accuracy* means *getting it right* then clearly we should be as accurate as possible when collecting data. *Precision* is something different. We could record the length of computer breakdowns to the nearest five minutes, to the nearest minute, or in theory even to the nearest second. In Table 1.1 they are implicitly recorded to the nearest minute (or perhaps in minutes ignoring any fraction of a minute). It is unlikely in practice that one would need a more precise record. Indeed it might suffice to record them only to the nearest five, or even ten, minutes.

Inaccuracy – gremlins in the data – can take many forms. Meters or recording instruments may malfunction or be misread. We all know the panic induced by a radio announcer who tells us 'the time now is five minutes past eight' when he means 'past seven'. Even BBC announcers misread studio clocks despite careful training! How easy to make a mistake, if it is not daily routine, in noting the time, reading a weight, measuring a length, or recording a voltage.

Numeral spoonerisms and *typist's stutter* are common sources of error. We write 23 when we mean 32 or type 23 as 223 or 233. It is easy too, especially if we do not divide the thousands off by commas or spaces, to write 1000000 when we really mean 100000. Did you have to look twice to see if I meant one hundred thousand or one million? Inaccuracies in recording and transcribing can only be kept to a minimum by careful checking. *The need for checking cannot be overemphasized when handling numbers.*

Precision and comprehension

It is easier to assess visually the pattern of numbers with only one or two digits than it is those with three or four; mental arithmetic is not too hard with such numbers. People used to dealing with figures can subtract 30 from 79 and see the answer is 49; and that adding 32 to 71 gives 103. Unless you are very good at mental arithmetic you will probably make a mistake in subtracting 31.7 from 78.1 in your head. It's not even easy to see immediately that the answer is something a little less than 50 unless we first *mentally* translate 31.7 to *a little over 30* and 78.1 to *nearly 80*.

In the era of cheap pocket calculators – not to mention home and business computers – it is seldom that we are forced to do mental arithmetic; but the simpler the pattern of numbers, the easier it is to abstract useful information quickly from them and to spot trends and exceptions. Some writers, including Ehrenberg (1983, Ch. 15), recommend that we prepare tables in a way that makes it easy to do mental arithmetic. The point is important, but there are other considerations when presenting data, and we discuss table layout further in Chapter 5.

Reducing precision loses some information but an opposite danger is the introduction of spurious accuracy. If we measure a person's height we usually record it to the nearest centimetre, or equivalently in metres expressed to two decimal places. Theoretically, when we say a man's height is 171 cm, we assert a belief that it lies between 170.5 and 171.5 cm. Could we, even if we wanted to, measure more precisely? Almost certainly not, as the *height* of an individual is not exact or immutable. Even if the subject does not deliberately slouch or stretch while we measure his or her height, two recordings by different observers or at slightly different times may differ by about 1 cm.

A warning

Example 1.3. Beware of introducing spurious accuracy when changing units. If heights are recorded in metres and we want to change them to inches we must divide by 0.0254. Dividing 1.71 by 0.0254 on my pocket calculator produces the answer 67.32283465!

Since human heights can only be recorded to the nearest inch or half inch at best, it would be sensible to convert 1.71 metres to 67 inches (or perhaps 67.5 inches if rounding to the nearest half inch). Never report a human height as 67.32283465 in., even if a computer print out produces such a figure. Such nonsenses are best avoided by programming the computer to print, in this case, to the nearest integer (i.e. whole number).

Example 1.4. Returning to the computer breakdown example, given a stopwatch we could in theory measure breakdown times to the nearest second (or even to the nearest 1/100 of a second). To attempt to do so would only introduce spurious accuracy. Many computer breakdowns may not be noticed for a minute or more after they occur. For example, if a fault occurs in a disc drive it may be first noted only at the next occasion we try to read from or write to a disc on that drive.

All this casts doubt on both the precision and accuracy of the times recorded in Tables 1.1 and 1.2. Some faults (typically CPU breakdowns) will be noted almost at the instant they occur. Others may be undetected for some time if a piece of equipment is only used intermittently. What is probably important in practice is the lag between detection and remedy. It is essentially this that is recorded in Table 1.1 with, from the practical viewpoint, very reasonable precision.

Significant and effective digits

Populations of cities or countries are often given to the nearest hundred, or even thousand. Thus if the populations of three cities are given as 51 200, 219 400, 583 100 we say they include respectively 3, 4 and 4 *significant digits* (i.e. the numbers of digits before the two terminating zeros). The final zeros are essential in specifying the magnitude of the populations but do not show whether, for example, the exact population of the first city is 51 219 or 51 243 or 51 201 or precisely 51 200. Similarly for decimal expressions such as 0.003 12, 0.071 25 or 0.000 01 we say the numbers of significant digits are respectively 3, 4 and 1. The zeros immediately after the decimal point establish the correct order of magnitude. In these three examples the *number of decimal places* is five in each case.

Very often we have data in which the leading digits are all the same, e.g. in successive months the production of cars by a factory might be 1215, 1293, 1242, 1217. Here the only digits that change are the tens and units digit. Ehrenberg (1983) suggests the term *effective digits* for these. This is a useful terminology.

Exercise 1.4. Table 1.3 gives the lengths in seconds of 100 success-ive intervals between cars passing a fixed point on a main road one Monday morning. The time is recorded to the nearest second, observations commencing at 10 a.m. The information was collected to obtain a picture of traffic density. We discuss this data in more detail in Chapters 6 and 17, so again you may like to make a copy of this table for later reference. From a visual inspection of the table, determine (a) the shortest and (b) the longest interval between passing cars. Do you get the impression of any trend or pattern? For example, is there a tendency for the interval between cars to increase or decrease as the morn-ing progresses; if there is a longish gap between the pass-ing of two cars does this invariably tend to be followed by a run of three or four cars close together? Can you spot any other trends or pattern?

Table 1.3. *Intervals between passing cars (seconds)*

3	11	1	12	23	16	8	10	8	2	6	18	14	11	17
16	6	12	2	8	36	23	8	7	3	6	7	5	7	26
55	14	1	16	6	47	7	5	1	2	9	5	14	10	17
23	2	4	31	7	8	4	4	29	43	4	1	17	3	14
10	6	10	2	4	3	6	10	25	13	10	10	11	3	2
11	9	3	4	25	9	18	4	22	5	14	1	6	13	3
34	4	3	7	2	3	3	8	22	1					

Exercise 1.5. For use in exercises in later chapters and as a data bank for trying out various techniques as we introduce them how about collecting some data of your own? See

how ingenious you can be. Here are some possibilities:

1. Keep a record of the numbers of telephone calls you make during one month and the duration (in seconds) of each.
2. If you smoke keep a count of the number of cigarettes you smoke each day for a month.
3. If you are a motorist record the number of miles covered on each trip you make, together with the start and finish time, also the total number of miles covered each day.
4. Record the time you spend on buses, trains, or other form of public transport each day.
5. If you catch regular buses or trains each day record for each trip the number of minutes late (or early) each is during a particular month both for your departure point and for arrival at your destination.
6. Keep a record of the time spent each day eating your dinner, together with information that will tell you how many times each main course dish was repeated in a month.
7. If you have a not too immaculate lawn you could divide it into a number of squares of side length 1 metre, say, and count the numbers of daisies and dandelions in each.

Before deciding what record you keep (and it need not be one of the above examples), give some thought to what use you intend to put the information. In Example 2 above, for instance, you might collect the data to see whether or not it confirms a feeling you have that you smoke less at weekends and on holidays than you do on a working day.

Seeking information

In Chapters 14 to 16 we discuss techniques for collecting information. It is important to ask the right questions and to frame them in a way that encourages relevant answers.

Would you be impressed by a survey seeking information on the ill effects of using Visual Display Units (VDUs) that heads sections of questions:

Pregnancy and VDU usage (women only)

Pregnancy and VDU usage (men only)?

Dr Pauline Topham drew attention to such a questionnaire in a letter to the Royal Statistical Society's *News and Notes*. She kindly supplied me with a copy of the questionnaire.

Despite the extraordinary headings the actual questions in each section did admit of sensible answers, the first question for men being 'Has your partner/wife experienced any problems in becoming pregnant since you have been working at a VDU terminal?' The question itself is not unreasonable, even if of doubtful relevance, but human nature being what it is the very heading of the section invites frivolous replies along the lines of 'Yes, but the milkman helped out.' We discuss this particular survey in more detail in Chapter 14.

2 Understanding tables

Ready-made tables

Collect your own data, and you know who to blame if you get it wrong! Most of us meet graphs or tables prepared by others. A full understanding of a table usually needs background knowledge – words to go with the numbers.

Example 2.1. Displays like Table 2.1 are a familiar feature of the sports pages of most British newspapers.

Table 2.1. *First Division*

	P	W	D	L	F	A	W	D	L	F	A	Pts
Liverpool	40	14	4	2	49	11	8	8	4	23	20	78
Man Utd	40	14	3	4	43	18	6	10	3	27	20	73
QPR	41	14	4	3	37	12	8	3	9	29	22	73
Southampton	39	15	4	2	44	17	5	6	7	17	20	70
Nottm Forest	40	13	4	3	45	17	7	4	9	27	27	68
Arsenal	41	10	5	6	41	29	8	4	8	32	29	63
West Ham	40	10	4	5	38	21	7	5	9	21	31	60
Tottenham	41	11	3	6	30	23	6	6	9	33	41	60
Aston Villa	41	14	3	4	34	22	3	6	11	24	37	60
Everton	40	8	9	3	18	11	6	5	9	22	30	56
Watford	41	8	7	5	34	30	7	2	12	32	46	54
Leicester	41	11	5	4	40	28	2	7	12	25	38	51
Luton	41	7	5	9	30	33	7	4	9	23	30	51
Norwich	40	9	8	4	34	20	3	6	10	12	26	50
Ipswich	41	10	4	6	32	22	4	4	13	21	34	50
Sunderland	41	8	9	4	26	18	4	4	12	14	35	49
WBA	40	9	4	6	27	23	4	5	12	18	37	48
Birmingham	41	7	6	7	19	18	5	5	11	20	32	47
Coventry	41	7	5	8	31	32	5	6	10	24	44	47
Stoke	41	10	4	6	26	23	2	7	12	14	40	47
Notts County	40	6	6	7	30	33	4	4	13	19	36	40
Wolves	41	4	8	9	15	28	2	3	15	12	48	29

Relevance and understanding

This table is doubtless boring to non-football followers, but it illustrates important principles that apply to the interpretation of many tables.

If you are interested in football you will understand the table easily, but if you are not very keen on the game and uncertain about some of its finer points, you will get only limited information from it. For example, you may know, or guess, that the team with the most points at the date the table was published (8 May 1984) is the current *league leader*, yet be unsure how points are awarded. The header 'Pts' above the last column is an abbreviation for 'points'. Thus you will conclude Liverpool are the league leaders, and Wolves are bottom of the league.

Does the table tell us who will be league champions in 1984? Must it be Liverpool? Could it be Manchester United? Or QPR? Or some other club? To answer these questions we need information *not* in the table.

In particular, we must know: (i) how many matches each team plays in a season; (ii) what points are awarded for a win, a draw or a defeat.

The answers are: (i) each team plays 42 matches, meeting every other team in the league once at home and once away; and (ii) a team receives 3 points for a win, 1 point for a draw and zero if it loses.

The champions

Now we can answer questions about the likely champions. The first column, headed P, gives the number of games already played. Liverpool and Manchester United each have $42 - 40 = 2$ more games to play. If Manchester United win both they will have 79 points. It is easy to see this is the only way they could pass Liverpool's present total of 78 points, for a win and a draw would only give them 77 points.

If Liverpool win at least one of the remaining fixtures they will have 81 points and thus cannot be beaten by Manchester United.

Suppose Liverpool draw one game and lose the other, while Manchester United win both games; then each would have 79 points.

Who would then be champions? To answer we need to know more about the rules. We must wait until the end of the season when we have a table for all games analogous to Table 2.1. The relevant rule is that if two teams then have the same number of points the team with the highest value of the goal difference D, where

$$D = \text{(goals scored by team)} - \text{(goals scored against team)}$$

wins the championship. We can get an indication of the team likely to have the highest value of D at the end of the season by calculating the present D values from Table 2.1.

Columns 2, 3, 4, 5, 6 headed 'W','D','L','F','A' give respectively the number of 'home' games won (W), drawn (D), lost (L) and the goals scored for (F) and against (A) each team; columns 7 to 11 give corresponding figures for 'away' games.

For Liverpool, adding the numbers in columns 5 and 10 (both headed F) we see they have scored 49 + 23 = 72 goals and from columns 6 and 11 we see they have had 11 + 20 = 31 goals scored against them, so D = 72 − 31 = 41. For Manchester United D = 70 − 38 = 32 (check this from the table). Only if Manchester United won with very high scores and the game lost by Liverpool was a really humiliating defeat could this difference change so that Manchester United got the better end-of-season goal difference.

What about QPR, with the same points as Manchester United in Table 2.1? They cannot win, for they have played forty-one games and can end the season with a maximum of 76 points – that only if they win their remaining game. Now try your hand at a couple of exercises.

Exercise 2.1.   We know from Table 2.1 that Manchester United could overtake Liverpool but QPR could not. What about Southampton? Is there any other team that could in theory still win the championship?

Exercise 2.2.   The three teams who end the season at the bottom of the first division have their problems, for they are automatically relegated to the second division. In Table 2.1

the teams at the bottom are Stoke, Notts County and Wolves, but Birmingham and Coventry have the same points as Stoke.

Answer the following:

(i) which teams, if any, are already certain to be relegated?

(ii) are the five teams named above the only possible teams to be relegated? If not, name any other possible relegation candidates.

For the record, at the end of the 1983–84 season Liverpool were champions and Birmingham, Notts County and Wolves were relegated.

Patterns in tables

What can we learn from Table 2.1 about patterns of performance? Let's compare home wins and away wins for each team. Look at all twenty-two teams and you'll see that all bar one have more home than away wins (the exception is Luton with seven home and seven away wins). You can easily verify that, closely related to this, with only three exceptions teams have scored more goals in *home* than in *away* games. Name the exceptions.

Exercise 2.3.   Find any exceptions to the general pattern that more goals are scored *against* a team in its away matches than in its home matches.

From our discussion of Table 2.1 some general points about understanding tables emerge. In particular:

1.   Some conclusions can only be drawn by combining information from the table with other knowledge (e.g. we must know how many matches each team plays in a season and the points allocation before we can say which teams are still championship contenders).

2.   Tables are often useful for highlighting trends (e.g. usually more home than away wins, the tendency for the difference D (goals for − goals against) to decrease as we move down the league table).

Our deductions are well known to football enthusiasts, but even if one has only a slight knowledge of the game or lives in a country where it is not played, the table is still quite informative on matters like the advantage of home games as reflected in goal tallies *for* and *against*.

When combining additional knowledge in interpreting tables, make certain you use information *relevant to the particular table*. A table analogous to Table 2.1 for the Scottish premier division would be interpreted differently because their system awards only two points for a win. In some competitions instead of goal difference, D, points ties are separated by the ratio

$$R = \text{(goals scored by team)/(goals scored against team)}.$$

If we wish we could also use Table 2.1 to find incidental information like how many London teams played in the league first division in 1983–84. We would need to know some UK geography and where each team had its headquarters. Is Sunderland a London suburb? Is Arsenal a London-based team?

A financial table

The financial pages of a newspaper provide our second example. To understand it we need to know something about stock markets.

Example 2.2.   Table 2.2 is a set of prices on 4 January 1984 for trusts managed by a company, HK Unit Trust Managers Ltd, who run a range of unit trusts. The complete newspaper table for all trusts occupied half a broadsheet page.

Investors' interests

If you have money to invest the penultimate column headed '*offer*' is important, for it shows the purchase price for a unit in any of the listed trusts. The column headed '*yield*' gives the percentage yield based on the current dividend. High yields are

Table 2.2. *Unit trust quotations 4.1.84,*
           HK Unit Trust Managers Ltd

1983/84

High bid	Low offer	Trust	Bid	Offer	Yield
56.0	43.0	American	55.5	59.2	2.20
29.2	27.0	Extra Inc	27.2	29.7	8.50
60.4	48.2	Commodity	56.4	60.7	3.40
59.8	42.0	Far East	59.8	64.4	1.10
45.1	38.8	Income	41.0	44.0*	6.90
54.1	32.6	Japan	54.1	57.6	0.20
38.5	25.3	Australian	38.5	41.0*	1.30
87.8	74.4	Small Co's	85.0	91.4	1.70
121.5	85.0	Technology	121.5	130.7*	0.20

*ex dividend.

associated with *income* trusts. Low yields do not necessarily mean
a trust is a poor investment; those with low yields may aim at capital
growth rather than income. The experienced investor will interpret
yields as an indication of trust aims as well as performance.

Sellers' interests and performance

A seller is interested in the column headed 'bid', which
tells him how much the trust management will pay if it buys back
units. It is always less than the day's 'offer' price.

The first two columns indicate how prices have changed in 1983–
84. Newspapers are often vague about this concept. The above table
was published at the beginning of 1984 so the period probably refers
effectively to the whole of 1983. However, when one gets to mid-
1984 it is not always clear whether such a heading covers the period
1 January 1983 to the current date, or simply the last twelve months.
This information should be available from the newspaper's finance
department or from the unit trust managers. The period should be
the same for *all* trusts listed in any *one* newspaper, but may not be
the same in different newspapers.

Columns 1 and 2 provide simple indicators of recent performance
for each trust. For example, we can easily verify that over the period

the largest possible percentage increase has been in the 'Japan' fund and the largest absolute increase per unit in the 'Technology' fund.

Some simple calculations

Make sure you know how to calculate the percentage increase for a fund. It is fairly obvious that if I bought units for 50p and sold them for 100p, my increase would be 100 per cent. Do you agree that the percentage increase between low offer and high bid in Japan units during 1983–84 is approximately 66 per cent?

Exercise 2.4. The absolute increase in Japan units is 54.1 − 32.6 = 21.5. What is it for Technology? Check the assertion made above that this latter fund shows the greatest absolute difference per unit.

Wise investment policy

An investor seeking capital gains aims for the greatest percentage increase.

The performance data in Table 2.2 enables us to ascertain: (i) how well an investor would have fared over the past year if he had purchased and sold at the optimum times; and (ii) whether a trust is or is not near its peak price over the past year; we do this by comparing current prices with the highest bid and lowest offer.

It is controversial whether past performance is a useful guide to future behaviour. Some financial advisers say never buy units at peak price; others tell you that a trust with a good recent track record is the one to buy. Tables like 2.2 are no help in reconciling these conflicting theories, but if you believe one of them, they do give an indication of track record and proximity to a peak.

Dividends

In the table three trusts are marked *ex dividend*. This means that if, on that day, you bought units in those trusts you would not receive a dividend that has been declared but not yet paid. However, if you now sell units you purchased *before* the dividend was declared you would still receive that dividend.

One may use the table to compare investment policies using fairly simple arithmetic. Try this in Exercise 2.5.

Exercise 2.5. Suppose you have £1000 to invest today. How many 'Australian' units would you get? (Do you know what unit trusts do if the amount you invest will not buy an exact whole number of units?)

If you had invested £500 in 'Commodity' units at the lowest offer price during 1983–84 and sold them at the highest bid price in that period how much capital would you have gained? If, instead of selling them at the highest bid, you had held them until 4.1.84 and sold them that day, how much would you have gained?

What have we learnt?

This example has shown that a small amount of data about each trust enables one to make general comparisons of performance. In the United Kingdom there are more than 700 approved unit trusts. Newspapers naturally aim to give as much useful information as possible about each trust in a relatively small space, so it is important to choose information that gives reasonable guidance.

Recapitulation

The main points we have made in this chapter are:

1. Interpretation of a table may need background information not in the table itself. Compilers of tables assume (sometimes unjustifiably) that anyone using the table will have that information.

2. Limited information (as in the unit trust table) may provide a basis for useful calculations, different features being of interest to different users of the table.

Some tables may not be presented in a form that makes them immediately useful; it may be necessary to modify them or produce new tables. This is a matter we consider in the next two chapters.

One important point we have not yet dealt with is the question of the layout of tables for ease not only of reading but of interpretation. For example, in Table 2.1 (as is usual newspaper practice) the spacing between all columns is the same. The table is easier to read and interpret if we put double spacing between columns 1 and 2, between columns 6 and 7 and between columns 11 and 12. Effectively this separates information for home and away fixtures and makes comparisons easier. In Table 2.3 we modify the earlier presentation in this way and insert two new headings — 'Home' and 'Away'. Do you not find the format easier to work with?

Table 2.3.   *First Division*

	P	Home					Away					Pts
		W	D	L	F	A	W	D	L	F	A	
Liverpool	40	14	4	2	49	11	8	8	4	23	20	78
Man Utd	40	14	3	4	43	18	6	10	3	27	20	73
QPR	41	14	4	3	37	12	8	3	9	29	22	73
Southampton	39	15	4	2	44	17	5	6	7	17	20	70
Nottm Forest	40	13	4	3	45	17	7	4	9	27	27	68
Arsenal	41	10	5	6	41	29	8	4	8	32	29	63
West Ham	40	10	4	5	38	21	7	5	9	21	31	60
Tottenham	41	11	3	6	30	23	6	6	9	33	41	60
Aston Villa	41	14	3	4	34	22	3	6	11	24	37	60
Everton	40	8	9	3	18	11	6	5	9	22	30	56
Watford	41	8	7	5	34	30	7	2	12	32	46	54
Leicester	41	11	5	4	40	28	2	7	12	25	38	51
Luton	41	7	5	9	30	33	7	4	9	23	30	51
Norwich	40	9	8	4	34	20	3	6	10	12	26	50
Ipswich	41	10	4	6	32	22	4	4	13	21	34	50
Sunderland	41	8	9	4	26	18	4	4	12	14	35	49
WBA	40	9	4	6	27	23	4	5	12	18	37	48
Birmingham	41	7	6	7	19	18	5	5	11	20	32	47
Coventry	41	7	5	8	31	32	5	6	10	24	44	47
Stoke	41	10	4	6	26	23	2	7	12	14	40	47
Notts County	40	6	6	7	30	33	4	4	13	19	36	40
Wolves	41	4	8	9	15	28	2	3	15	12	48	29

Exercise 2.6. Look at any tables you can find in newspapers (the *Financial Times* or the business section of *The Times* are happy hunting grounds), periodicals, books, reports, etc., preferably selecting tables on a topic you know something about. Are the examples you select informative? Easy to read and interpret? Could you set them out in a better way? Do you feel they lack information likely to be needed by the people for whom they are intended?

3 Organizing data

Ordering data

What about indigestible data like that in Tables 1.1 and 1.2? How can we make it more palatable, or its message clearer?

Example 3.1. Table 1.1 can be used to answer questions about the proportion of breakdowns less than thirty minutes, or less than one hour, or more than a hundred minutes; but to do so quickly and easily we use it as a source for *derived tables or graphs*.

Glancing at it (for convenience we reproduce it below but you may find it handy to have a photocopy as we suggested in Chapter 1), we see that while many breakdowns last less than half an hour, an appreciable number last over a hundred minutes. The classical way of making the pattern clearer is by setting up a table (called a frequency table) showing how many breakdowns last, say, less than ten minutes, how many at least ten but less than twenty minutes, how many at least twenty but less than thirty minutes and so on. Setting up this table is straightforward but tedious because we have to do a lot of counting. We could look at Table 1.1 and count the number of entries of 9 or less, then the number between 10 and 19

Table 1.1 (Repeated). *A company record of computer downtime in minutes, May 1984*

49	18	123	3	87	21	7	24	11	19	243	38
11	18	32	101	6	32	27	41	3	25	19	242
122	15	7	6	2	18	42	24	7	9	14	10
30	23	141	7	102	83	29	11	15	7	6	8
121	4	23	42	18	31	25	42	6	339	19	27
12	11	3	5	9	3	22	17	20	5	3	18
142	51	18	41	9	9	27	14	33	128	34	18
232	179	143	181	6	14						

inclusive, and so on. Doing it that way is a recipe for errors. It is an ideal job for a properly programmed computer; many have library programs (*software* is the jargon term) to do just this.

A pencil and paper method

To do the job with pencil and paper, set about it methodically. In a column at the left of a page write 0–9, beneath it 10–19, below that 20–29 and so on as in Table 3.1. Then work systematically through the observations in Table 1.1 and, for each, record a vertical bar or 'tally' on the appropriate line as in Table 3.1. Since the first entry in Table 1.1 is 49 the first bar goes in the 40–49 group, the next, corresponding to 18, goes in the 10–19 group, then a tally in the 120–129 group for 123 and so on. To make it easier to add, once we have

Table 3.1.   *Downtime distribution scoring by vertical bars*

Downtime (mins)	Count	No. occasions
0–9	‖‖‖ ‖‖‖ ‖‖‖ ‖‖‖ ‖‖‖	24
10–19	‖‖‖ ‖‖‖ ‖‖‖ ‖‖‖ ‖‖	22
20–29	‖‖‖ ‖‖‖ ‖‖‖	13
30–39	‖‖‖ ‖‖	7
40–49	‖‖‖ ‖	6
50–59	‖	1
60–69		0
70–79		0
80–89	‖	2
90–99		0
100–109	‖	2
110–119		0
120–129	‖‖	4
130–139		0
140–149	‖‖	3
150–159		0
160–169		0
170–179	‖	1
180–189	‖	1
190–229*		0
230–239	‖	1
240–249	‖	2
250–329*		0
330–339	‖	1
Total		90

four tallies in any one group we do not record the next entry by a vertical bar but rather by putting a stroke through the four bars already there. To get the total in any group we just add the completed groups of five and any remaining vertical bars. Table 3.1 is the end product.

Long periods such as 190–229 and 250–329 in which there are no breakdowns have been 'lumped together' as a space-saving device and marked with an asterisk for clarity.

Using Table 3.1

A glance at Table 3.1 tells us quickly about relative durations of breakdowns. We see that of the ninety breakdowns 24 + 22 + 13 = 59 last less than half an hour. A further set of fourteen last between thirty minutes and one hour. Of the remainder, sixteen are fairly well scattered between about one and four hours with a slight clustering around two hours (nine between 100 and 150 minutes). One major downtime is on its own, lasting more than five hours.

A manager calling for this information may be particularly worried about downtimes over one hour; there are seventeen of these, nearly one fifth of all breakdowns. This may alarm him. He can tolerate short breakdowns; they do not lose his firm much money – but his directors, and computer users, may be agitated about longer breaks. He may call in computer experts and ask why breakdowns occur and what can be done about them. Table 3.1 suggests there may be several kinds of breakdown – short ones by far the most common and easily remedied. In broad terms something like two-thirds of all breakdowns last half an hour or less, but it is longer ones lasting over an hour that are really worrying. Should reserve equipment be purchased for use during failures? Should part of the equipment that is causing these longer breakdowns be replaced or modified? Should we have a stand-by engineer to make repairs more quickly? The answers are a matter of commercial judgement. In the next chapter we see that information like that in Table 1.2 provides a useful basis for answering this type of question.

Exercise 3.1. What percentage of machine breakdowns last thirty minutes or more, but less than two hours?

Improved presentation

Can we improve on the presentation in Table 3.1? The tally marks are useful for setting up the table, but when it comes to using it they are a distraction and are best omitted from a final version. More importantly, it is clear we have lost some information in this table. We no longer know the *exact* length of stoppages. Can we do something to give us the advantages of this table without losing so much information, yet involving little extra work? The answer is yes. We replace it by a *stem and leaf* display. This is a comparatively recent but simple and useful idea suggested by American statistician John Tukey (see e.g. Tukey (1977, Ch. 1) or Erickson and Nosanchuk (1979, Ch. 2)).

Stem and leaf displays

Example 3.2. From Table 3.1 we see there are thirteen observations between 20 and 29. Their common feature is that each has a 'two' as the tens digit. The second (unit) digit may be any one of 0, 1, 2, 3, 4, 5, 6, 7, 8 or 9.

Let us proceed much as we did in forming Table 3.1, but in the first column where we had, say, the entry 20–29 we simply write 2. Similarly corresponding to entries 0–9 we write 0, 10–19 we write 1, 30–39 we write 3, 90–99 we write 9, 100–110 we write 10, 330–339 we write 33 and so on. That is, in this first column we put the tens digit (preceded by a hundreds digit when there is one). Now go through Table 1.1 as we did in forming Table 3.1, but instead of a vertical bar for each entry we put instead the actual units digit for each number in the appropriate row. This is how we build up a stem and leaf display. The numbers in the first column are the *stems* and the digits in the rows corresponding to each stem are the *leaves* attached to that stem.

The procedure is shown in Table 3.2. The stems are in the leading column. To save space, where we have a long run of stems with no

Table 3.2.   *Stem and leaf display of*
computer breakdowns (stage 1)

Stem	Leaf
0	3 7 6 3 7 6 2 7 9 7 7 6 8 4 6 3 5 9 3 5 3 9 9 6
1	8 1 9 1 8 9 5 8 4 0 1 5 8 9 2 1 7 8 8 4 8 4
2	1 4 7 5 4 3 9 3 5 7 2 0 7
3	8 2 2 0 1 3 4
4	9 1 2 2 2 1
5	1
6	
7	
8	7 3
9	
10	1 2
11	
12	3 2 1 8
13	
14	1 2 3
15	
16	
17	9
18	1
*	
23	2
24	3 2
*	
33	9

leaves, as with stems from 19 to 22, these are simply indicated by an asterisk. We fill in the leaves much as we did the vertical bars in Table 3.1, *except* that we put the actual digits and do *not* separate them into groups of five.

Thus, working from Table 1.1, where the first entry is 49 we put a 9 in the leaf section of the row for stem 4. The second entry, 18, implies a leaf of 8 on stem 1, next a leaf of 3 on stem 12, then a leaf of 3 on stem 0. Proceeding in this way, the final entry gives a leaf of 4 on stem 1 for the last entry of 14 in Table 1.1. It is a good idea to place a vertical rule between stems and leaves.

Note that we have labelled Table 3.2 *stage 1* of the stem and leaf display; very often this is all we need. If we require it, *stage 2*, the final stage, is obtained simply by rearranging the leaves on each stem in ascending order. This we have done in Table 3.3, appending a column giving the number of leaves on each stem (we could easily

Table 3.3.   *Stem and leaf display of
computer breakdowns (stage 2)*

Stem	Leaf	No.	Cumu-lative total
0	2 3 3 3 3 3 4 5 5 6 6 6 6 6 7 7 7 7 7 8 9 9 9 9	24	24
1	0 1 1 1 1 2 4 4 4 5 5 7 8 8 8 8 8 8 8 9 9 9	22	46
2	0 1 2 3 3 4 4 5 5 7 7 7 9	13	59
3	0 1 2 2 3 4 8	7	66
4	1 1 2 2 2 9	6	72
5	1	1	73
6		0	73
7		0	73
8	3 7	2	75
9		0	75
10	1 2	2	77
11		0	77
12	1 2 3 8	4	81
13		0	81
14	1 2 3	3	84
15		0	84
16		0	84
17	9	1	85
18	1	1	86
*			
23	2	1	87
24	2 3	2	89
*			
33	9	1	90

do this in Table 3.2 if we wished). These equal the numbers of obser-vations in each of the groups in Table 3.1. The last column, labelled *cumulative total*, gives, corresponding to each stem, the number of observations on that stem and all stems above it. We shall find this useful in Chapter 6, Example 6.1.

Table 3.2 is as easily compiled as Table 3.1 yet it retains the full numerical information in the raw data *apart from the time order in which the observations arose*. Preparation of Table 3.3 from 3.2 is straightforward and we end up effectively with a complete ordering, in increasing duration, of the breakdown times, as well as the num-bers in each ten-minute interval.

Like Table 3.1, Table 3.3 illustrates clearly the concentration of breakdowns of short duration represented by the large numbers of leaves on the stems 0 to 5. There is a much smaller cluster of leaves around stems 10 to 14. The asterisks draw attention to large breaks or sets of stems without leaves. There is a small clump of three breakdowns at the 23, 24 stems and one isolated leaf on stem 33.

In Chapter 6, p. 73, we show how to get a set of numbers called a *five-number summary* that condenses key information from a stem and leaf diagram.

It is easy to write a computer program to produce tables like 3.3. Computers are particularly good at sorting data into ascending or descending order. Many standard program packages have a facility to do just this.

Used in association with a five-number summary, Table 3.3 is a very useful representation of the raw data of Table 1.1.

Exercise 3.2.   Table 3.4 lists asking prices for three-year-old Ford Escort cars in the advertisements in one issue of a motoring magazine. Choosing appropriate stems (the stems need not be the leading digit, or the tens digit, as in our previous example), represent the data on a stem and leaf display. Comment on any interesting features of the data and suggest possible explanations for them.

Table 3.4.   *Asking prices for three-year-old Ford Escort cars*

2495	2750	2999	3300	2700	2945	2995	2400	3250	3175
2000	3100	3199	2850	2750	2900	2950	3150	3395	3250
3175	2995	3000	2900	2450	2500	2775	2950	3100	3125
2725	3100	3450	3500	2875	2975	3125	2700	2745	2850
2900	2895	3199							

Exercise 3.3.   In Exercise 1.5 we invited you to collect some data of your own. If it seems appropriate, represent it on a stem and leaf display. For some data a stem and leaf display is not appropriate. If you think it is not for any data you collected, explain why.

We have dealt only with simple stem and leaf displays; there are a number of practical variations described in the references given on p. 37.

Histograms

There is one other popular representation that can be based on either
Table 3.1 or 3.3; this is a graphical picture called a *histogram*.

It is often a question of personal preference whether particular
information is best presented as a graph or a table. For relatively
small amounts of straightforward data I generally prefer tables as
they usually contain all the information that one can get from a
graph, and more as well. Nevertheless graphs often give a useful
qualitative picture and, as we shall see in Chapters 8, 9 and 10, they
may be invaluable for summarizing complicated information.

Example 3.3. Take a sheet of paper (graph paper is preferable for
accurate results with minimum effort). Along the bottom of the sheet
mark a base line or axis with thirty-five equally spaced dividing
marks (see Figure 3.1). Starting from the left on this axis, label the
first dividing mark zero, count five marks along and label that mark
50, then count a further five marks and put a label 100 and so on.
(You could, if you wish, label the marks intermediate between 0 and
50 as 10, 20, 30, 40; those intermediate between 50 and 100 as 60,
70, 80, 90, and so on.)

Now draw a rectangle rising from this base with corners at the
'zero' and 'ten' divisions. The height of this rectangle, on an appropriate scale shown on the left vertical axis, is to be twenty-four units
(the number of breakdowns of less than ten minutes' duration in
Table 3.3). The vertical scale should be so chosen that twenty-four
units (the maximum number on any stem) requires most of the page
height. Next, since there are twenty-two breakdowns between 10
and 19 inclusive, we draw, adjacent to the first rectangle, a second
of height twenty-two units on the base sector between 10 and 20,
next a rectangle of height thirteen is put beside this to represent the
thirteen breakdowns that are at least twenty minutes, but less than
thirty minutes' duration. We continue this way, representing the
numbers of breakdowns in each ten-minute interval by rectangles of
appropriate height until Figure 3.1 is complete. It helps interpretation to write in each rectangle the number of observations it represents, but this is not essential as it can be obtained from the scale
on the left. Although not common practice to include these numbers,

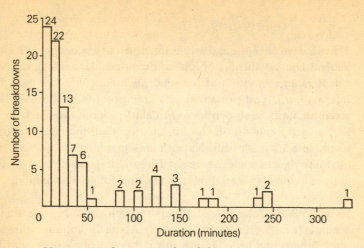

Figure 3.1. Histogram of computer breakdown times.

it is a useful device if one wants to look at detail as well as general pattern.

We have introduced one possible source of confusion. We cannot tell from the graph alone whether an observation of exactly 20, for example, is included in the rectangle on base 10 to 20 or on base 20 to 30. Our convention has been to include observations exactly on a dividing point in the rectangle to the right of that point. The convention should be made clear in explanatory text accompanying a histogram. Alternatively, rather than labelling the divisions 0, 10, etc., we might put a label between the first two divisions reading 0–9, between the next two divisions 10–19, etc., to indicate that these are the numbers associated with each rectangle.

This is a useful *at a glance* representation of the numbers of breakdowns of various durations. The numbers are proportional to the areas of the rectangles. But Table 3.3 really does the same job, and more! In fact it incorporates what is essentially a histogram tipped on its side. Since each single-digit leaf represents a unit, the number of breakdowns in a particular interval is equal to the number of *leaves* on the stem corresponding to that interval, i.e. the number of leaves in the relevant row of Table 3.3. If Table 3.3 is held on its side it gives a similar picture to Figure 3.1 and has the added advantage that we can obtain individual breakdown durations from it.

Even if we have been a little scathing about histograms, in a more general context graphs are not to be despised, as we shall see in Chapters 8 to 10.

Exercise 3.4. Present the data in Table 3.4 on a histogram.

Exercise 3.5. In Exercise 1.5 you collected your own data. Can it be sensibly represented on a histogram? If so, prepare a histogram. For some data this may be impossible, but other graphical techniques we shall develop later may be applicable.

4 Rearranging data

More derived tables

Table 1.2, pp. 15–16, provides detailed information about computer breakdowns. It helps us to answer questions like:

1. How many downtimes involve the CPU?
2. How many involve the printer?
3. On how many days are there more than one breakdown?
4. During the month which component has the most breakdowns?
5. Do any pieces of equipment show a tendency to break down more than once per day?
6. What is the duration pattern of breakdowns for the printer?

Questions like these are best answered by *abstracting* the relevant data from Table 1.2 and presenting it in auxiliary tables. Table 1.2 (have you a copy handy?) is a good working record, compiling information about failures as they occur; but it contains detail that is often irrelevant to answering specific questions. We need an array of sub-tables, each relevant to a particular query.

Example 4.1. The production manager wants to know about printer breakdowns. He asks, 'On how many days do we have zero, one, two, . . . , breakdowns?'

Exercise 4.1. Using Table 1.2 record on how many days in May 1984 there are 0, 1, 2, . . . , 9 printer breakdowns. Present your results in a table.

Does your table look like, and agree with, Table 4.1? Of course, the way it is set out there is not the only way to present the data. It would be equally valid to place it in two columns headed respect-

Table 4.1. *Printer failures during May 1984*

No. of failures	0	1	2	3	4	5	6	7	8	9
No. of days observed	20	5	3	1			1			1

ively *Numbers of failures* and *Numbers of days observed.* There is nothing sacred about the exact wording of the row or column headings. They should be succinct but informative.

If the data in Table 1.2 were stored in a computer it would be simple to write a computer program to produce Table 4.1, but do this only if a similar task had to be undertaken a number of times; perhaps for monthly data for several machines or for a single machine over several years.

Note that the total number of failures in the month is obtained by multiplying the corresponding entries in each row of Table 4.1 and adding, i.e. total number of failures is

$$0 \times 20 + 1 \times 5 + 2 \times 3 + 3 \times 1 + 6 \times 1 + 9 \times 1 = 29.$$

The entries in the second row total thirty-one, the number of days in May, providing some check on the accuracy of the tabulation. One should also check after completing Table 4.1 that there are indeed twenty-nine printer failures during the month. This requires a count of all printer failures in Table 1.2, easily done by scanning column 3 of that table. Such checks are extremely important. In forming any but the simplest derived tables *it is the exception rather than the rule to make no mistakes at the first attempt.*

Example 4.2.   A production manager may want more information about printer failures. He may wish to know how these are distributed throughout the month, i.e. the actual dates on which there are one or more failures, and have the duration of each tabulated in, say, ten-minute intervals. This more elaborate information is given in Table 4.2, again by extracting the relevant material from Table 1.2.

Exercise 4.2.   Look at the format of Table 4.2 (but not at the detailed entries) and repeat for yourself its preparation from Table 1.2. Then check your effort against Table 4.2.

Table 4.2.   *Daily distribution and duration of printer failures*

Day	Duration (minutes)						
	0–9	10–19	20–29	30–39	40–49	50–59	60+
1					1		
2							
3							
4	1		2				
5		2					
6							
7							
8							
9			1				
10	1						
11		1	1				
12							
13	3	2			1		
14							
15	3	2	1	1			2
16							
17							
18							
19							
20							
21	1				1		
22							
23							
24							
25							
26							
27	1						
28							
29							
30	1						
31							

Table 4.2 tells a lot about printer breakdowns throughout the month. There was a bad patch from 10–15 May (pretty obvious from Table 1.2 itself). Things look up in the latter part of the month; only four breakdowns after 15 May and three of these of less than ten minutes' duration. The pattern is rather typical of a piece of equipment that at some stage develops a fault that is hard to iron out but which, once this is corrected, then behaves quite well. Table 4.2 has one weakness, a lot of blank space. This makes it difficult to see immediately in which row and column a particular entry lies and may result in misreading. Have I misread if I claim there is one breakdown of 40–49 minutes' duration on 22 May?

The table may be condensed by leaving out any rows or columns devoid of entries, reducing it to Table 4.3. A space between dates (rows) indicates a period with no entries. Some economy in space is gained in moving from Table 4.2 to 4.3, and we have made things more explicit by classifying the two *over sixty-minute* breakdowns into the appropriate ten-minute intervals. Such minor improvements can often be made when a table is recast. There is one slight loss of clarity. The table must be studied more closely to appreciate the fall-off in printer breakdowns in the latter part of the month.

Table 4.3. *Reduced summary of Table 4.2 data*

Day	Duration (minutes)						
	0–9	10–19	20–29	30–39	40–49	100–109	140–149
1					1		
4	1		2				
5		2					
9			1				
10	1						
11		1	1				
13	3	2			1		
15	3	2	1	1		1	1
21	1				1		
27	1						
30	1						

Example 4.3. The manager may want a more elaborate summary. He may ask for the numbers of breakdowns and their duration under the various categories listed in column 3 of Table 1.2. Table 4.4 uses Table 1.2 as a source, and illustrates our point on p. 16 that column 3 of that table provides a basis for classification.

An example of the value of cross-checks arose when I was preparing this table. Even after two checks I had recorded one disc drive

Table 4.4. *Duration of downtimes in various components*

Length	Routine service	CPU	Printer	Tape reader	Disc drive	Graph plotter	Total
0–9		2	11	6	3	2	24
10–19		3	7	6	5	1	22
20–29		1	5	2	2	3	13
30–39		1	1	2	1	2	7
40–49		1	3		1	1	6
50–59		1					1
*							
80–89		1		1			2
*							
100–109		1	1				2
*							
120–129		3			1		4
*							
140–149		2	1				3
*							
170–179		1					1
180–189		1					1
*							
230–239		1					1
240–249	1			1			2
*							
330–339	1						1
Totals	2	19	29	18	13	9	90

breakdown as a printer fault, giving a total of thirty printer faults. A check with my calculation on p. 45 based on Table 4.1 showed my mistake. Another useful check is provided by final column totals. They should, and do, agree with the totals in Table 3.1 on p. 35.

The above table displays a wealth of information with a clarity not shared by Table 1.2. With twenty-nine breakdowns, the printer is the most unreliable part of the system, although many failures in this unit are of only short duration. The number of breakdowns of the CPU is less than two-thirds the number for the printer, but there is a greater spread of associated downtime. The next highest frequency of breakdowns is in the tape reader, followed by the disc drive and graph plotter. The two routine servicings involve long downtimes.

Relative merits of tables

In Table 4.4 we lose some valuable information we had in Table 1.2. Before reading on, can you spot it?

It is the information on dates when breakdowns occur and the fact that some units tend to have bursts of trouble – a bad day or a run of bad days, e.g. for the printer the period 10–15 May (Tables 1.2, 4.2 and 4.3). We also see from Table 1.2 that the CPU had a bad spell near the end of the month (29, 30 May) and the tape reader had an off day on 23 May.

Can we improve the layout of Table 4.4? It might be just that little bit easier to spot patterns if we arranged the columns so that those with the highest total (bottom line) occurred on the left, falling away to the lowest total on the right. This involves rearranging the column order to printer, CPU, tape reader, disc drive, graph plotter, routine service. I do not recommend this reordering because 'routine servicing' and 'CPU' breakdowns are essentially different in character from peripheral faults; potentially more important, as they almost certainly imply complete closure of the system. Indeed it might be worth inserting a vertical rule between the columns labelled 'CPU' and 'Printer' in Table 4.4 to indicate that columns to the left involve the whole computer while those to the right may involve just the named peripheral. For technical reasons, in printed tables minimize the use of vertical rules (they cost money!). Note that in Table 4.4 we have already arranged columns involving the peripherals in order of decreasing totals from left to right – a good idea.

Other tables could usefully be derived from Table 1.2, depending on the information required. Some examples are given in the following exercises.

Exercise 4.3.   Suppose you have drawn up Table 4.3 but your boss now says he wants a table showing duration in minutes for each printer failure rather than classification into ten-minute intervals. Privately curse him for not making that clear at first, then prepare an appropriate table for him. If someone's requirements are not clear it pays to ask for clarification if tedious or unnecessary juggling of data is involved.

Exercise 4.4.   Use the information in Table 1.2 to prepare tables analogous to Tables 4.2 and 4.3 for CPU failures.

Counts

Data often consists of counts – typical examples are the *numbers* of faulty items produced in a batch of components, the numbers of cars passing an observation point on a road each minute, the numbers of strokes each player takes to play a hole in a golf match.

Example 4.4.   Table 4.5 gives the numbers of inward telephone calls received by an office switchboard in each one-minute interval between 10 a.m. and 11 a.m. one morning.

If an office manager faces complaints that his switchboard operators cannot handle the numbers of incoming calls, clearly he or she

Table 4.5.   *Inward calls per minute*
          between 10 a.m. and 11 a.m., 18 Jan. 1985

2	3	1	0	4	2	2	2	5	1	1	3	1	0	4	2	1	3	4	2
1	2	3	1	0	2	1	0	3	5	6	8	4	9	7	6	8	7	5	3
4	3	2	1	0	4	6	1	2	3	3	2	1	1	4	0	2	1	1	3

would want information like that in Table 4.5 not just for one hour on one day, but for several complete working days or for selected hours over a period of weeks. An obvious thing to do with data of this type is to draw up a *frequency table* giving the numbers of intervals (here each of one minute) in which 0, 1, 2, 3, . . . calls are received. Proceed as we did in forming Table 3.1, indicating in the appropriate row by a vertical bar each occasion 0, 1, 2, 3, 4, 5, . . . calls are received and group the bars into sets of 5 (4 vertical with a horizontal slash for the fifth) just as we did in Table 3.1. Table 4.6 results. The first column contains entries 0 to 9 (since 9 is the highest entry in Table 4.5). The first entry in Table 4.5 is 2, so we place a vertical bar in the row labelled 2, then a vertical bar in the row corresponding to 3, for the second entry. We proceed in this way until we have recorded all sixty entries. The final column of Table 4.6 gives the totals.

Table 4.6.   *Frequency table of calls received*

Number of calls	Number of times recorded	Total
0		6
1		14
2		12
3		10
4		7
5		3
6		3
7		2
8		2
9		1
	Total	60

In practice, since the vertical bars are only for counting convenience it is conventional to rewrite (certainly for publication) the frequency table without these, giving Table 4.7.

Recording the total of sixty gives a check that we have not missed any observations (or recorded any twice) – something very easy to do, especially when dealing with more extensive data. A correct total does not guarantee we have the right count for each number of

Table 4.7.   *Frequency table of*
            calls received

Number of calls	Number of times recorded
0	6
1	14
2	12
3	10
4	7
5	3
6	3
7	2
8	2
9	1
Total	60

calls. A double check against the original data is needed to confirm this.

Some deductions and limitations

From Table 4.7 we see that in all but eleven of the one-minute intervals four or fewer calls are received, i.e. in less than 20 per cent of the intervals does the switchboard operator have to deal with more than four calls per minute. A load exceeding four calls per minute might well put a strain on a single operator. Depending on switchboard layout and whether operators had to deal with outward calls at the same time, experiments might be made to see if two operators could cope adequately. In practice such decisions would certainly be based on observations for more than just a single hour!

Note that in going from Table 4.5 to 4.7 to make the frequency pattern clearer, we have lost one important piece of information. In the second half of the second row of Table 4.5 (representing the period from 10.30 to 10.40 a.m.) there is real pressure on the operator. The numbers of calls per minute 6, 8, 4, 9, 7, 6, 8, 7, 5, 3, are consistently more than during the rest of the hour. In planning switchboard operations it may be important to detect a tendency for calls to peak over a short period; an additional operator might be diverted temporarily from other duties to deal with such peaks if they are a daily recurrent feature.

While preparing tables like 4.6 from Table 4.5 one often spots incidentally characteristics of the original data – like the peaking just mentioned – that tend to become lost in the new form. Always keep a note of these. One disadvantage of assigning the preparation of such tables to a computer is that special features are less easily spotted than if we dirty our hands with the real data right from the start.

Exercise 4.5. How might you present the data in Table 4.7 in a graphical form similar to a histogram?

Exercise 4.6. Use Table 1.2 to draw up a frequency table for the numbers of breakdowns in hourly intervals throughout the day, i.e. determine for how many the starting time is in the interval 0800–0859, for how many in the interval 0900–0959 and so on to the interval 2300–2359. Do breakdowns seem to be more frequent at certain times of day?

Exercise 4.7. Is any of the data you collected in Exercise 1.5 appropriate for presentation in a frequency table? If so, construct such a table for it.

5 More sophisticated tables

Alternative presentations

In this chapter we look at different ways of presenting the same or closely related information. Generally speaking there is no best way of presenting facts *per se*. What is preferred depends partly on how information is obtained – more importantly on the use to which it will be put.

Example 5.1. Table 5.1 gives information about full-time under-graduate students in each of the Scottish universities in the academic years 1975–76 and 1980–81.

How good?

How accurate and precise are these statistics? Every number in the first four columns ends with a zero digit. Is this surprising? The logical explanation is that the data has been rounded 'to the nearest ten'. This clearly is the chosen degree of precision (see p. 18). Is it a sensible choice?

It probably is. Almost certainly there will be slight inaccuracies in data of this type. Some students who enrol at the beginning of a year drop out through illness, disillusionment, inability to keep up with the work, etc. Again, it is not always completely clear which students are full-time and which are part-time; this will be self-evident in the majority of cases but each university may have slightly different rules about how many courses constitute full-time study. When it comes to dividing students into Scottish or other domiciles, again the decision is not always clear cut. Is the daughter of a Texan who considers himself domiciled in Texas but whose family lives in Aberdeen during his five-year contract working on a North Sea oil rig domiciled in Scotland?

Table 5.1. *Full-time undergraduate students
at Scottish universities*

University	Scottish domiciled		All domiciles		Per cent Scottish domiciled	
	1975–6	1980–1	1975–6	1980–1	1975–6	1980–1
Aberdeen	4020	3970	4700	4980	86	80
Dundee	1390	1600	2420	2690	58	59
Edinburgh	6120	6060	8060	8560	76	71
Glasgow	7730	8340	8280	9070	93	92
Heriot-Watt	1890	2160	2500	2880	75	75
St Andrews	1500	1380	2740	3150	55	44
Stirling	1370	1570	1880	2700	73	58
Strathclyde	4350	5110	4960	5670	88	90
Total	28 370	30 200	35 540	39 690	80	76

Source: Scottish Education Department, *Statistical Bulletin*, February 1983.

The figures of 4700, 1600, 2500, 1500, 2700 appearing in the table may result from genuine rounding to the nearest ten, but it is possible they may, for various reasons, just be less accurate; perhaps rounded to the nearest hundred. There could be legitimate reasons for certain figures being less precise than others. Where there appears to be more than usual rounding it could be because in a particular year, or university, records are not readily available for a specific category like 'Scottish domiciled' and some sort of estimate or 'guesstimate' of numbers is all that can be managed. Now try an easy exercise in checking.

Exercise 5.1.   Check the totals in each of the colums; are there any anomalies? If so, how might they be explained?

Well, did you find some 'errors'? Adding, the total for 1980–81 Scottish domiciled students comes to 30190, not 30200 as recorded. That for all domiciles in the same year is also out by 10. This discrepancy is not hard to explain. It is attributable to round-off error.

Note that although marked as 'Total' the percentages given in the total row for the final two columns are not totals, but percentages based on the total numbers in the earlier columns.

Exercise 5.2.   Check the assertion just made about the percentages in the total row so that you are certain you know how they are calculated.

Reasonable rounding

Clearly all percentages in Table 5.1 are rounded to the nearest integer. With rounding to the nearest ten in the student numbers this is sensible. For example, for St Andrews in 1980–81 we see that 1380 from a total of 3150 students are domiciled in Scotland. The corresponding percentage is (1380/3150) × 100 = 43.81 if we round to two decimal places. However if the 'true' total student number were 3146 of whom 1384 were domiciled in Scotland we would still get, on rounding to the nearest ten, the totals in the table, but accurate calculation of the percentage now gives (1384/3146) × 100 = 43.99. Clearly with our precision in recording student numbers, decimal fractions in a derived percentage are meaningless.

Precision versus clarity

Table 5.1 was extracted from a larger table that gave corresponding information for 1979–80 and also data for full-time postgraduate students. It is common in official statistics to give data as precisely as is reasonably possible. For many uses less precise data might suffice, but the range of applications of official statistics is such that there are likely to be some users for whom high precision is essential. In Table 5.2 we give the same data to a lower precision than Table 5.1, yet for quick reference it gives a clearer overview of the main differences in student population and of the proportion domiciled in Scotland for the several universities. However if someone bet you that Stirling had fewer Scottish domiciled students than Dundee in 1980–81 you would need Table 5.1 rather than Table 5.2 to settle the argument.

Other formats

Table 5.1 lists universities in alphabetical order. This is handy for picking up an individual university, but results in a 'mixture' of information for large and small universities. For a much longer list involving hundreds of institutions alphabetical ordering is nearly always desirable. For short lists, if one wants a table to exhibit general patterns or exceptions it is sometimes better to order by some other characteristic such as size of institutions. In Table 5.2 universities are arranged in decreasing order of total undergraduates in 1975–76. We have also reordered the columns, giving totals before Scottish domiciled; a trivial alteration but it focuses attention on *total* size as a feature likely to be of prime interest. The table quickly gives a picture of how the Scottish universities compare in size and is useful to answer questions of the type: Is the proportion of Scottish domiciled students related to the size of a university?

Try answering that question using Table 5.1. You will find your eyes darting up, down and across the table several times before you come up with answers. It's easier with Table 5.2. In it we have thrown away some precision, giving student numbers to the nearest 100 (and in units of 100, i.e. 47 means 4700 students).

Table 5.2. *Full-time undergraduate students (hundreds)*
          at Scottish universities

University	All domiciles		Scottish domiciled		Per cent Scottish domiciled	
	1975–6	1980–1	1975–6	1980–1	1975–6	1980–1
Glasgow	83	91	77	83	93	92
Edinburgh	81	86	61	61	76	71
Strathclyde	50	57	43	51	88	90
Aberdeen	47	50	40	40	86	80
St Andrews	27	31	15	14	55	44
Heriot-Watt	25	29	19	22	75	75
Dundee	24	27	14	16	58	59
Stirling	19	27	14	16	73	58

The patterns

Table 5.2 brings out patterns; Scotland has two large universities, each with over 8000 undergraduates, two medium-sized institutions, Strathclyde and Aberdeen, each with about 5000 undergraduates, and four smaller universities. Three of the smaller universities have a lower proportion of Scottish domiciled students than have the larger universities. To further interpret these findings one needs information additional to that in the table. First of all we note that both Glasgow and Strathclyde (each situated in Glasgow) have 'in round figures' about 90 per cent Scottish domiciled students while for Edinburgh and Heriot-Watt (both in Edinburgh) the percentage is near 75. These figures reflect a tradition very strong in South-west Scotland, but less so in the Edinburgh area, that one should attend one's local university. The high proportion of Scots at Aberdeen is similarly accounted for by that university being regarded widely as the 'appropriate' university by many Aberdonians and also by most Highlanders. These prejudices in favour of 'local' universities in certain parts of Scotland run contrary to tradition in other parts of Scotland, and more generally in the United Kingdom, where choice of a university is influenced by factors such as an institution's reputation in particular disciplines, entrance requirements, or perhaps a pleasant environment, reinforced very often by a belief that it is 'good' for students to go to a university well away from their home town.

In this table, like so many, there is at least one figure that tends to go against general trends. The odd figure is one for Stirling in 1975–76, where, with a very low total enrolment, a relatively high proportion are Scottish domiciled. A table extending over further years would show this to be atypical for that university.

St Andrews has the lowest proportion of Scottish domiciled students. This probably reflects the fact that it has a small local catchment area relative to Glasgow, Edinburgh or Aberdeen and that it has some appeal to English traditionalists in that it is the oldest Scottish university and one of a handful in the UK that cling to certain Oxbridge-type traditions. The table does not tell us this. This is external information that helps to explain certain figures in the table.

I have dealt with this example in some detail to indicate how interpretation of quantitative data is generally inseparable from some explanation of the background (recall the football league tables). Remember our three main methods of communication are by words, numbers and pictures (including graphs, maps and diagrams). Quantitative data demands the use of numbers, but tables or graphs alone seldom tell the full story. The satisfactory interpretation of data demands a judicious blending of tables, graphs, maps, diagrams or other pictures, with words.

Turning the tables

In Chapter 4 we derived tables that were essentially sub-tables or condensations of larger tables. It is not uncommon to have to manipulate basic data to exhibit facets of interest more clearly.

Example 5.2. Table 5.3 is extracted from the Central Statistical Office's *Monthly Digest of Statistics*, the figures being available in several issues during 1983–84. It gives total numbers of passenger cars produced in various categories. We discuss these, then explore a further aspect – proportions of total production in these categories.

Table 5.3. *UK passenger car production, 1982*
(Monthly totals are for four or *five week period)

Month	Total	1000cc or under	Over 1000 to 1600cc	Over 1600 to 2800cc	Over 2800cc	Weekly Average
Jan	70 451	20 434	36 933	9 108	3 976	17 613
Feb	88 371	23 081	51 394	9 520	4 376	22 093
Mar*	98 563	27 110	55 276	10 877	5 300	19 713
Apr	65 495	15 672	39 379	6 954	3 490	16 374
May	80 938	17 367	50 718	9 024	3 829	20 235
Jun*	82 028	20 664	47 568	10 530	3 266	16 406
Jul	59 222	10 709	40 117	6 340	2 056	14 806
Aug	51 395	14 878	26 651	6 485	3 381	12 849
Sep*	64 754	9 166	45 878	6 558	3 152	12 951
Oct	77 808	15 002	51 212	7 630	3 964	19 452
Nov	73 767	12 883	50 620	6 187	4 077	18 442
Dec*	74 887	10 187	51 930	8 323	4 447	14 977

Source: *UK Monthly Digest of Statistics*, CSO/HMSO, 1983.

Not as perverse as it looks

The note in parenthesis at the head of the table about some months being four weeks while those marked with an asterisk are five weeks is not a monument to statistical perversity, but reflects the idiosyncrasies of the Gregorian calendar. Many firms keep records on a weekly basis. Practice has shown that confusion is reduced if a firm is asked to complete a return, say, on the last day of each month, for all working weeks *ending* during that month.

It is then inevitable that in some months (not necessarily the same ones in different years) some returns will be for five rather than four weeks. Obviously if weekly production rates remain nearly constant a higher output will be achieved in a 'five-week' month. But due to holiday periods, strikes, etc., even without the four/five week complication, production figures are not steady from month to month. The final column in Table 5.3 gives the average weekly production for any month and is obtained by dividing the monthly total by five in those months (five-week months) marked with an asterisk. For the other months we divide the monthly total by four. These weekly averages are fair comparators.

Choosing the categories

You may wonder why, in Table 5.3, production is broken into the categories 1000cc. and under, over 1000cc. to 1600cc., etc. The decision is somewhat arbitrary but reflects common sense. Effectively the categories break production records into small cars, medium family or business cars, large executive cars and very large specialist or luxury cars. There's little real difference in size and performance between many a 1598cc. car and a 1607cc. car, but a line has to be drawn somewhere and for many purposes associated with the motor trade the above divisions are satisfactory.

Table 5.3 is fine for anyone who wants to know general patterns of total production but it is not easy for picking out, for example, any trends in the *proportions* of cars of different sizes. One can look at particular parts of the table and note interesting features. For example total production in July at 59222 units is down from 82028 in June. This is partly due to June being a five-week month but also no doubt to July including a portion of the annual holiday period for some manufacturers. The drop is particularly marked for cars of 1000cc. and under. The figure falls from 20 664 to 10 709 – a nearly 50 per cent drop. The table itself does not explain why the drop is most marked in this category. Possibilities are that the holiday pattern is different in plants making different sizes of car or that plants making larger cars get back into production more easily and quickly after holidays than those making smaller ones.

For some purposes the production figures in Table 5.3 may be more precise than we need. Try forming a simpler table as an exercise.

Exercise 5.3.   If we want only to study the general pattern of trends we may get lost in the detail of Table 5.3. Derive from it a simpler table that just gives the information to the nearest thousand (i.e. in units of thousands of cars for each category).

In Table 5.3. for simplicity of reading we split off the 'thousands' from the 'hundreds' digit by a break, writing, for example, 27 110 rather than 27110. This is some help in preparing your table in Exercise 5.3 for, to the nearest thousand, 27110 becomes simply 27. Be careful though when you have to round; for example 27 853 rounds to 28!

When you have completed your table have a good look at it and see if you can detect any trends or characteristics that did not strike you so forcibly when looking at Table 5.3.

Proportions

If we are interested in the proportion of each month's production in the various categories, we need a modification of Table 5.3, ideally a table of percentages. These are easy to obtain. For example, in July, 6340 out of a total production of 59 222 are in the *Over 1600cc. to 2800cc.* category. This represents a percentage of $(6340/59 222) \times 100 = 11$ per cent (to the nearest integer, i.e.

whole number). Unless some very high or very low percentages are common in certain categories (and small differences in these are of interest) it is easiest to make comparisons if percentages are quoted to the nearest integer.

Table 5.4 gives the percentage of total monthly production in each of the categories in Table 5.3.

Table 5.4.   *UK passenger car production, 1982*
(Percentage of monthly production in each category)

Month	1000cc or under	Over 1000 to 1600cc	Over 1600 to 2800cc	Over 2800cc
Jan	29	52	13	6
Feb	26	58	11	5
Mar	28	56	11	5
Apr	24	60	11	5
May	21	63	11	5
Jun	25	58	13	4
Jul	18	68	11	6
Aug	29	52	13	7
Sep	14	71	10	5
Oct	19	66	10	5
Nov	17	69	8	6
Dec	14	69	11	6

The striking and easily spotted features of Table 5.4 are: (i) production of cars over 1600cc. remains a fairly steady proportion of the total throughout the year; and (ii) apart from a hiccup in the prime holiday month of August there appears to be a fairly steady decline in the proportion of 1000cc. and under matched by a corresponding increase of the proportion over 1000cc. but under 1600cc.

Anyone with a lively curiosity may well ask if this is a feature that is repeated every year or whether it signals a longer-term shift in production proportions (presumably reflecting market requirements) from very small to medium cars. Proportions for the early months of 1983 are given in Table 5.5 and indeed suggest the proportions in the small and medium range are in that period stabilizing near the 'late 1982' levels.

Table 5.5 also suggests there is now a drop in the proportion of cars over 1600cc.

Table 5.5.   *UK passenger car production, 1983*

   (Percentage of monthly production in each category)

Month	1000cc or under	Over 1000 to 1600cc	Over 1600 to 2800cc	Over 2800cc
Jan	14	70	11	5
Feb	17	67	11	5
Mar	20	65	9	5
Apr	20	71	5	4
May	18	70	8	4
Jun	18	69	8	4
Jul	18	73	6	4

Exercise 5.4.   The percentages in each row of Tables 5.4 and 5.5
should in theory add to 100. Why? Check if they do. If any
do not, explain why not. Do any discrepancies worry you?

Percentages and proportions

A percentage is a part *per hundred*. A proportion is a decimal or
fractional part of unity. To convert a proportion to a percentage
we multiply by 100. Thus a proportion of 0.69 corresponds to a
percentage of 69. Many people are happier with percentages than
with straight proportions. The reason is not entirely clear, but one
may be a preference for whole numbers rather than decimals or
fractions. But if we say, for example, 51.73 or 29.24 per cent of a
population have such and such a characteristic we give ourselves
the worst of both worlds. There is an arbitrariness in the popular
choice of parts per hundred rather than, say, parts per thousand or
parts per ten thousand as a yardstick. It is perfectly permissible,
though not common practice, to express a percentage of 69.3 as 693
parts per thousand. Scientists who have to deal with small amounts
of substances often talk of parts per million. Seven parts per million
is more readily comprehended than a proportion of 0.000 007, or
0.000 7 per cent.

   The widespread preference for percentages is probably justified if
we confine ourselves to integral values, for it gives us a conceptual
basis that we can visualize fairly well – we can think readily in two-
digit numbers (see p. 19).

One weakness that percentages have is that 1 in 3, 1 in 6, 1 in 8 – all commonly occurring proportions – do not have integral percentage equivalents, being respectively, to two decimal places, 33.33 per cent, 16.67 per cent and 12.5 per cent. However, as we move ever more rapidly to the metric system based on multiples of ten this becomes of decreasing importance. In practice percentages are likely to remain the popular way of expressing proportions.

Collecting information into a table

Example 5.3. Suppose a coach company is starting up services between five Scottish cities – Edinburgh, Glasgow, Dundee, Aberdeen and Inverness. The distances by road between each of these cities are known and in devising a timetable the coach company will know the journey times required (not necessarily in exact proportion to the mileages as the times will depend upon the number of stops en route and the nature of the roads joining each city). This information could be given to passengers as separate items for each of the ten possible routes, e.g. Edinburgh to Dundee: Distance 53 miles, journey time 1 hour 35 minutes; Aberdeen to Inverness: Distance 104 miles, journey time 3 hours 10 minutes, etc.

It is easy to verify that there are ten different 'pairings' of the five towns. Such descriptions for each pairing become tedious and it is not easy to pick out any particular one. We can get all this information into one simple table with rows and columns headed with the names of the cities. Table 5.6 is an example. In the top right of the table are the distances between cities and in the bottom left the journey times.

Table 5.6. *Distances* (**miles**) *and travel times (hrs. mins) between cities*

	Edinburgh	Glasgow	Dundee	Aberdeen	Inverness
Edinburgh	—	**44**	**53**	**118**	**158**
Glasgow	1.10	—	**76**	**142**	**169**
Dundee	1.35	1.55	—	**65**	**130**
Aberdeen	3.25	3.55	1.45	—	**104**
Inverness	3.45	4.20	3.00	3.10	—

To find the distance between Glasgow and Aberdeen, for example, we enter the row labelled 'Glasgow' and the column headed 'Aberdeen' and read from the top portion of the table the entry 142, i.e. from Aberdeen to Glasgow is 142 miles. Similarly entering the row labelled Aberdeen and the column headed Glasgow we find the entry 3.55 indicating that the journey time between these cities is 3 hours 55 minutes. Check from the table that from Edinburgh to Dundee is 53 miles and the journey time 1 hour 35 minutes as asserted earlier. Tables with these rectangular patterns are known as *arrays* (or sometimes as *matrices*). Note that running diagonally from top left to bottom right we have blanks (or zeros) as there is zero distance between any city and itself!

Multiway tables

Example 5.4. Some tables classify data in several ways. Table 5.7 is based on information in the *Monthly Digest of Statistics* for July 1985. It shows the numbers of male and female agricultural workers (in thousands) in the UK for each of the years 1977, 1980 and 1983. Nature of employment (regular full-time, regular part-time and seasonal) is also given.

It is an example of a *multiway classification table*.

Anyone using tables like this will probably be interested in totals; totals for each sex, how many are in each employment category, irrespective of sex, etc. Showing these sub-totals in Table 5.7 would

Table 5.7. *Agricultural workers (thousands), classified by job, sex, year*

	1977	1980	1983
Males			
Full time	184	163	152
Part time	36	32	31
Seasonal	54	57	57
Females			
Full time	20	17	15
Part time	34	32	29
Seasonal	42	43	41

make it cluttered. It is better to supplement such a table by three separate two-way tables, one classifying by years and employment categories (combining sexes), one by years and sex (combining employment categories) and perhaps one by employment categories and sex (combining years). In these tables the *marginal totals* for each classification can be given without clutter. Table 5.8 gives a breakdown by years and employment categories (i.e. we add the number of employees for the two sexes in each job category).

Table 5.8. *Agricultural workers (thousands),*
classified by job and year

	1977	1980	1983	*Total*
Full time	204	180	167	551
Part time	70	64	60	194
Seasonal	96	100	98	294
Total	370	344	325	1039

The last entry of 1039 in this table is obtained as either the sum of the row totals above it or as the sum of the column totals to the left of it, providing a partial check on the calculation of those sub-totals.

Table 5.9 gives a breakdown by sex and years based on Table 5.7. Check carefully that you understand how it is formed. The column totals, as they obviously should be, are the same as in Table 5.8.

Table 5.9. *Agricultural workers (thousands),*
classified by year and sex

	1977	1980	1983	*Total*
Males	274	252	240	766
Females	96	92	85	273
Total	370	344	325	1039

Exercise 5.5. Prepare a table analogous to Tables 5.8 and 5.9 for workers classified by employment category and sex (i.e. combining years). Consider any checks you have on accuracy by comparison with totals in Tables 5.8 and 5.9. Do you agree if I assert that this is unlikely to be a very useful table in practice?

Exercise 5.6. Examine the appropriate tables (some or all of Tables 5.7 to 5.9) to see what trends or changes you note in numbers of agricultural workers between 1977 and 1983. What other interesting information can you glean from the tables?

In Chapters 3 to 5 we have by no means exhausted the possibilities for laying out tables, nor discussed all possible types of table that can be derived from basic data. The possibilities are nearly endless, but there is little point in rearranging a table or deriving new tables unless the result is going to be useful. In Chapter 7, Table 7.3, p. 87, we shall meet an example of a table of very limited usefulness.

6 Simple data summaries

A data *précis*

Remember Table 3.3, p. 39? It gave a rearrangement of the Table 1.1 data in ascending order of breakdown durations. Of the ninety downtimes it told us that twenty-four were less than ten minutes and a further twenty-two were between ten and nineteen minutes. This implies 24 + 22 = 46, or just over half, lasted less than twenty minutes. So you might reasonably say an average breakdown lasts about twenty minutes.

Can we find a few numbers that give us a good idea of the data pattern? There are some obvious candidates.

The middle value

Find the middle value and we know half our observations are at or below it; the same number at or above. This is an obvious candidate for any data *précis*.

If we have five observations, all different, it is easy to arrange them in ascending order. The third is clearly the middle value; the first and second lie below, the fourth and fifth above. There may be two minor problems about middle values, both easily resolved. Suppose two values are equal and they themselves lie in the middle in the sense that we have in our five observations a smallest value, a second smallest value, then two larger but equal values and finally a fifth value larger than any of the others, e.g. the values might be 2, 5, 8, 8, 11. The third ordered value (for which two observations tie) is 8. There are now two below 8, one above and two 'tie' on the value 8. We still regard the third observation of 8 as the middle value. In a more extreme case we may have a string of equal values, e.g. 1, 6, 6, 6, 6. In this case our middle (third) value is still 6.

The other minor complication occurs with an even number of observations; six for example. Which is our middle observation? If they all differ and we take the third we have two below and three above; if we take the fourth we have three below but only two above. The obvious compromise is to take a value between the third and fourth observation; what better than that half-way between? Thus, if six observations arranged in ascending order are 2, 7, 8, 11, 15, 16, the 'middle' observation is half-way between the third (8) and fourth (11) i.e. $(8 + 11)/2 = 9.5$.

The 'middle' observation has a special name: the *median*. In general, if we have any number, n, of observations *arranged in ascending order*, then if n is odd the median is the $(n + 1)/2$th observation. For example, with 73 observations the median is the $(73 + 1)/2 = 37$th observation. If n is even the median lies midway between the $n/2$th and the $(n + 2)/2$th observation, e.g. with 74 observations the median lies half-way between the $74/2 = 37$th observation and the $(74 + 2)/2 = 38$th observation. If the 37th ordered observation was 49 and the 38th was 63 the median would be $(49 + 63)/2 = 56$. If the 37th and 38th observations *both* had the same value, 52, say, the median would be 52.

Example 6.1.   For the ninety observations in Table 3.3, the median is half-way between observation *number* 45 and observation *number* 46. From the final column of the table we see that 46 observations are less than 20 and the largest of these 46 ordered observations are 19, 19, 19 (see the second row of Table 3.3 and remember how we formed our stem and leaf display). It is clear these are the 44th, 45th and 46th *ordered* observations. Thus the median is 19.

Minimum, maximum and range

The lowest and highest numbers recorded are also of interest. From Table 3.3 (or indeed from the original Table 1.1, although a little less readily) we see these to be respectively 2 and 339.

Their difference $339 - 2 = 337$, called the *range*, measures the total spread of the data. Using the median and the smallest and largest values and remembering in broad terms that half the observations lie above and half below the median, we can also compare spread *above* and *below* the median. Values at or below the median run from 2 to 19, a spread of $19 - 2 = 17$. Values at or above the median run from 19 to 339, a spread of $339 - 19 = 320$. So there is a much greater spread in the top half of the *distribution* of breakdown times; this difference is a reflection of *skewness* as opposed to *symmetry* (implied by near equality). However, these measures of relative spread are strongly influenced by the two extreme values. While there are a number of breakdowns near the lower extreme of two minutes (in all there are nine of five minutes' or shorter duration), the one breakdown of 339 minutes is somewhat isolated. Had it not occurred, our longest breakdown would have been only 243 minutes, very nearly 100 minutes less. We therefore seek more stable measures for overall spread and to indicate skewness. This suggests basing our measures on something less dependent on two special observations, the largest and smallest.

Quartiles

So far we have found:

Median 19

Greatest value 339

Smallest value 2

Range 337

Suppose we determine the 'medians' of two subsets of observations; one subset being the observations below the actual median, the other being the subset of observations above it. The 'median' of the lower subset essentially gives for all observations a dividing point with one-quarter of *all* observations below or at it and three-quarters at or above. So a name suggesting *quartering* is appropriate. It is called the *first (or lower) quartile*. The 'median' of the subset of observations that lie above the median for all observations is called the *third (or upper) quartile* because it has three-quarters of all observations below or at it and one-quarter at or above. What about the *second quartile?* It has two-quarters (i.e. one-half) of the observations at or below it, so it is the median. As with determination of medians, there are a few points to watch so that we define first and third quartiles consistently and uniquely. Books on statistics adopt varied conventions for this, but they tend to lead to only minor differences except with very small data sets. I have argued elsewhere (see Sprent [1981, pp. 57–59]) that the most logical way to define the rth quartile (r = 1, 2, 3) for a set of n observations is that it is given by the (rn/4 + ½)th observation. Remember the second quartile is just the median. Quartiles defined this way are either integral *observation* numbers or an integer plus a fractional part – either ¼, ½ or ¾ . A *fractional part* of an observation is to be interpreted as that fraction of the difference between the observation corresponding to the integral part and the next observation. Thus if the rth quartile is the 17.75th ordered observation and the 17th observation is 19 and the 18th is 25 then the rth quartile lies three-quarters of the way between 19 and 25, i.e. it has the value 23.5. You may need to read this a couple of times to get it right!

Example 6.2. Table 6.1 gives the quartile *observation number* for values of n between 30 and 35. Thus if n = 33 then n/4 = 8.25; adding ½, i.e. 0.5, we see the first quartile is the 8.75th observation. The second quartile or median is the (2 × 8.25 + 0.5) = 17th observation. This agrees, as it should, with our earlier rule for determining medians. The third quartile (make certain you see why) is the 25.25th observation.

Other conventions used to define quartiles give slightly different

Table 6.1. *Quartile observation numbers*
for n ordered data

n	1st quartile	2nd quartile	3rd quartile
30	8	15.5	23
31	8.25	16	23.75
32	8.5	16.5	24.5
33	8.75	17	25.25
34	9	17.5	26
35	9.25	18	26.75

observation numbers from those in Table 6.1 for the first and third quartiles, the differences becoming less pronounced the greater the number of observations, and being of little practical consequence. Our rule is simpler than most.

Example 6.3.   Applying the rule to the data in Table 3.3 with $n = 90$ we find the first quartile is the $(90/4 + \frac{1}{2}) = 23$rd observation and the third quartile is the 68th observation. We have already observed that the median is the 45.5th observation and equals 19.

The 23rd observation is easily seen to be 9, since there are 24 observations below 10 and the last four of these – the 21st, 22nd, 23rd and 24th – are all 9. There are 66 observations at or below 39, so clearly from Table 3.3 the 67th and 68th ordered observations are each 41.

Interquartile range

What use can we make of the first and third quartiles? In broad terms (ignoring for the moment observations exactly at a quartile), one-quarter of the observations lie below the first quartile and one-quarter lie above the third quartile. It follows that half the observations lie between the first and third quartiles.

Denote the first and third quartiles by Q_1 and Q_3 respectively. Then $Q_3 - Q_1$ gives the spread of the 'central half' of the observations. For the data in Table 3.3 this spread is $41 - 9 = 32$. It is called the *interquartile* range.

The greater the interquartile range, the greater the spread of the 'centre half' of the observations. It provides an alternative measure of spread to that given by the range, i.e. (greatest – least) observation. It is more stable as it depends on the general pattern of observations and not just on two extreme values. It is less influenced by taking additional observations which may well include a single 'freak' value. Extreme observations, such as the greatest or least, often reflect some unusual circumstance and may be atypical readings. In Table 3.3 for example, could 339 be a misrecording of 39 (see p. 18)? However, in our discussion in Chapter 4 we accepted this as a genuine downtime for routine servicing of the computer.

Indeed one argument for keeping detailed records like those in Table 1.2 is that the additional information may help to confirm whether a particular observation is 'reasonable'. Clearly from Table 1.2 (and more obviously from Table 4.4) and in broad common-sense terms, not unexpectedly, routine servicing leads to lengthy downtimes.

Skewness

Denote the median by M. The differences $Q_3 - M$ and $M - Q_1$ are of interest. Each of these ranges spans one of the two 'quarters' of the observations centred about M. If the differences are approximately equal it suggests a fairly symmetric allocation on each side of M (at any rate for those observations between Q_1 and Q_3) but if $Q_3 - M$ is much larger than $M - Q_1$ there is an appreciably greater spread above the median. This situation is often referred to as *positive skewness* or *skewness to the right*, this term becoming self-explanatory when we discuss graphical representation in Chapter 9, p. 119. If $M - Q_1$ noticeably exceeds $Q_3 - M$ we say we have *negative* skewness or *skewness to the left*.

Denoting the greatest and least values by G and L respectively, we often (but by no means invariably) find the difference between $G - M$ and $M - L$ behaves in a similar manner to that between $Q_3 - M$ and $M - Q_1$, confirming symmetry or skewness as the case may be.

Five-number summaries

We have suggested five numbers L, Q_1, M, Q_3, G that are easily calculated once data has been arranged in ascending order. Written in this order they form a *five-number summary* of the data, a term introduced by Tukey (1977).

Example 6.4. For the computer breakdown data we have L = 2, $Q_1 = 9$, M = 19, $Q_3 = 41$, G = 339, so we write the five-number summary

(2, 9, 19, 41, 339).

This summary enables us to say most of the things about the data that we have discussed above. Breakdowns last from 2 to 339 minutes; half of them are of 19 minutes' or less duration. Three-quarters are less than 41 minutes, one-quarter less than 9 minutes. The 'central half' of the downtimes *distribution* lies in the interquartile range of width $41 - 9 = 32$ minutes. Since $Q_3 - M = 22$ while $M - Q_1 = 10$ only, there is a suggestion of positive (right) skewness. This is reinforced by the difference $G - M$ being 320 while $M - L$ is only 17.

A five-number summary tells us a lot about data pattern, carrying messages in particular about:

1. *Centrality or location*: given by the median (half the observations above this value; half below).

2. *Range or spread*: measured by range, $G - L$ or, to avoid over-influence from extremes, by interquartile range, $Q_3 - Q_1$.

3. *Symmetry or skewness*: near equality of $Q_3 - M$ and $M - Q_1$ implies reasonable symmetry; gross inequality suggests skewness; the message is often reinforced by the behaviour of $G - M$ and $M - L$.

Sometimes, even in cases with little difference between $Q_3 - M$ and $M - Q_1$, we may find a large difference between $G - M$ and $M - L$. When $G - M$ is the larger we say the distribution of observations has a long *upper* or *right* tail; if $G - M$ is the smaller we speak of a long *lower* or *left* tail. With the computer breakdown data there is clearly a long *right* tail. The origin of the term *right* tail is obvious from the histogram in Figure 3.1.

Now for some practice.

Exercise 6.1.   A chemist analyses leaf samples from thirty different plants and determines the magnesium content in parts per million dry weight. The values he obtains are 6, 9, 13, 7, 18, 24, 11, 31, 9, 8, 41, 11, 8, 15, 20, 39, 51, 22, 6, 8, 4, 23, 21, 18, 3, 7, 31, 9, 5, 8. Represent this data on an appropriate stem and leaf display. Form a five-number summary and consider its interpretation.

Exercise 6.2.   Did you make a copy of the data in Table 1.3 as suggested? Use it (or turn to the table, p. 21) to arrange the data in a stem and leaf display and form a five-number summary and consider its interpretation. (Note that a stem need not always be a tens digit and that not all stems need be the same size – e.g. one might have the first stem ranging over five digits, the next over seven, the next over twelve and all following ones over ten digits if this gives a display that is easier to interpret. However, in this example I suggest taking all stems the same size.) Generally speaking, unless the data set is very large, the stem and leaf display loses some of its usefulness if more than one or two stems have appreciably more than twenty leaves each.

If you form an appropriate display (see Chapter 21, p. 278, if you have difficulty – but do not turn to this until you have tried hard) you will find the five-number summary is

(1, 4, 8, 14, 55).

Clearly the distribution is *skew* and *long tailed* to the right. The median is 8 and the interquartile range, $Q_3 - Q_1 = 14 - 4 = 10$.

Means

Once data has been arranged in order it takes only a few moments to produce a five-number summary. But given only the original or 'raw' data of Table 1.1 arrangement in order is time-consuming. We saw in Chapter 3 that we may want to do this for several reasons. However, if we are not doing this for purposes additional to obtaining a median, it may be easier to calculate other measures that tell us where a distribution is centred and something about the spread.

A measure of *centrality* or *location* that, at least until recently, has been more popular than the median is the *arithmetic mean* or average (often just called *the mean*). You probably know that it is obtained by adding all the observations and dividing by the total number of observations. Sometimes the *mean* has a value very close to the median, but not always.

Example 6.5. With a pocket calculator (or micro-computer) you will easily find the sum of the observations in Table 1.1 is 4042. Divide 4042 by 90 and the answer, 44.9, is the mean. Look now at the five-number summary, p. 73. The third quartile has the value 41; since three-quarters of the observations lie at or below 41, clearly three-quarters or more lie below the mean and one-quarter or less above it. Indeed if we turn to Table 3.3, p. 39, we see that 71 observations are below 44.9 and only 19 above!

For this data, then, the mean does not seem a very good measure of centrality, yet it is widely used in data analysis.

The intuitive appeal of the median is that we know it represents the 50–50 point – there are as many observations at or below it as there are at or above it. If there is a completely *symmetric* placing of observations above and below the median then the mean and median coincide.

Example 6.6. Here is a very simple example where mean and median coincide. Consider the observations

5, 8, 10, 12, 15

Clearly the median is 10; it's simple mental arithmetic to see the observations sum to 50, so the mean is also 10. Note here the symmetry. The value 10 is the median; the value 8 is 2 *below* 10 and 12 is 2 *above* 10; 5 is 5 *below* 10 and 15 is 5 *above* 10.

However, the mean and median may still coincide when there is not perfect symmetry. Consider the observations 2, 4, 10, 12, 22. The median is still 10; so is the mean, but clearly the observations are not symmetric.

In general mean and median coincide if the *deviations from the median* have a simple property; namely, the magnitude of the sum of the *negative* deviations from the median equals the sum of the *positive* deviations. For the first data set above, the negative deviations are $5 - 10 = -5$ and $8 - 10 = -2$, a total of -7, i.e. their *magnitude* is 7. The positive deviations are $12 - 10 = 2$ and $15 - 10 = 5$, totalling 7. Similarly in the second set it is easily seen that the negative deviations from the median are -8 and -6, total -14. The positive deviations are 2 and 12, total 14.

Example 6.7. Here are some observations where mean and median differ:

3, 5, 10, 12, 15

The median is obviously still 10 but the mean is 9 (check this). The sum of negative deviations from the median is −12 and of positive deviations is 7. The two sums have a different magnitude. If we consider the deviations from the mean value 9, the sum of negative deviations is −10, and the sum of positive deviations, i.e. 10 − 9, 12 − 9 and 15 − 9, is 10.

The mean is in fact a measure for which the sum of positive deviations from it *always* equals in magnitude the sum of negative deviations. Only when the median coincides with the mean does the median share this property.

While the *same number of observations at or above and at or below* gives an intuitive appeal to the median as a measure of *location* or *centrality* we now see that the property of the mean that the sum of positive deviations equals the sum of negative deviations justifies the mean as another intuitively appealing measure of centrality. When they differ markedly the median might be regarded as more 'typical' of observations as a whole.

For reasonably symmetric distributions mean and median do not differ greatly in value. The mean has certain desirable mathematical properties when we want to make inferences from data – a matter we take up in a little more detail in Chapters 16 and 17.

Exercise 6.3. What is the mean of the observations in Table 1.3, p. 21?

The answer you should get is 10.94. Note that positive or right skewness implies the mean is likely to be greater than the median. Why?

Variance and standard deviation

The concept of the median as the second quartile and the idea of 'quartering' ordered observations makes it logical to associate the median as a measure of location with interquartile range as a measure of spread.

For mathematical and statistical reasons, most of which we shall no more than hint at in this book, there is sound logic in using a rather more complicated measure of spread when we use the mean as a measure of location. The appropriate choice is called the *standard deviation*. It in turn is simply the positive square root of another measure of spread called *variance*.

Essentially variance is the mean of the sum of the squares of the deviation of all observations from the mean. That sounds a mouthful, but a simple numerical example makes it less forbidding.

Example 6.8.   Consider the observations

3, 5, 10, 12, 15

with mean 9, already used in Example 6.7, p. 77. Thus the deviations of the observations from the mean are respectively -6, -4, $+1$, $+3$, $+6$. The squares of these deviations are 36, 16, 1, 9, 36. The mean of the squares of the deviations is obtained by adding these and dividing by the number of observations, here 5. The variance is thus

$$(36 + 16 + 1 + 9 + 36)/5 = 98/5 = 19.6$$

The *standard deviation* is the positive square root of this, i.e. 4.43. A pocket calculator helps, but using it you will likely get an answer like 4.427188724 (depending on how many decimal places are displayed). In practice it is sensible to give the standard deviation to no more than two extra *significant figures* than there are in the original data. This implies that for a set of general integral values we might give the standard deviation to no more than two decimal places, but if we had observations such as 1200, 1300, 1600, 1800, 2300 we should give the standard deviation to no more than the nearest integer because the final 00 is not significant for observations rounded to the nearest hundred.

The above method of calculating standard deviation explains the concept but is not a good method in practice as we see from a further simple example.

Example 6.9.   Consider three observations 1, 13, 50. Their sum is

64 and the mean is 64/3 = 21.3333 rounded to 4 decimal places. Normally it is sensible to record the mean of integers to no more than one decimal place and here rounding to one decimal place gives a mean of 21.3. Unfortunately this round-off has a cumulative effect on calculations of variance when we have appreciable amounts of data.

Practical calculations of variance

We make calculation easier and more accurate by using a different set of rules, proceeding as follows:

Step 1. *Square each observation and obtain the sum of the squares.* For the data set in Example 6.9 the squares are 1, 169, 2500 with sum 1 + 169 + 2500 = 2670.

Step 2. *Sum all the observations, square the sum and divide by the number of observations.* We have seen that the above data set sums to 64 so $(64^2/3)$ = 1365.333.

Step 3. *Subtract the result of step 2 from that of step 1,* i.e. 2670 − 1365.333 = 1304.667.

Step 4. *Divide by the number of observations.* The answer is the variance. For this example 1304.667/3 = 434.89.

The above steps are easily carried out and may be dovetailed on a modern calculator.

The standard deviation is the square root of the variance, i.e. 20.85.

Warning: many pocket calculators are programmed to calculate standard deviations. If you have a calculator with such a program try it to calculate the standard deviation of 1, 3, 50. Do not be surprised if the answer you get rounds to 25.54. Neither this nor our answer,

20.85, is wrong! Blame the statisticians; they use *standard deviation* for two different concepts. We shall come to this distinction in Chapter 16, p. 214. The difference arises at step 4 where, instead of dividing by the number of observations (in our example 3), the calculator program may divide by 2 (one less than the number of observations). In practical problems with more observations the difference is less dramatic. If, with 100 observations, our rules gave a standard deviation of 17.32, a pocket calculator dividing by 99 instead of 100 would come up with 17.41. For 1000 observations it would give 17.33 if our rule gave 17.32.

Check any calculator (or micro-computer) program with a simple example like ours to see what it actually calculates. If, after rounding, it gives neither of the above answers ask a trained statistician to show you what it really does.

Exercise 6.4.   The first twenty observations in Table 1.3 are:

3   11   1   12   23   16   8   10   8   2

6   18   14   11   17   16   6   12   2   8

Use the rules given above to calculate the standard deviation of these twenty observations.

If you have the stamina (or a micro-computer with a program to calculate standard deviations) repeat the exercise for the full set of 100 observations in Table 1.3!

The answer for the full set is 10.27. An interesting feature of this result is that it is quite close to the mean of 10.94. In Chapter 17 (p. 224) we show that this has important theoretical implications.

Exercise 6.5.   We gave the rule for calculation of a mean as *divide the sum of the observations by the total number of observations*. If you apply this rule to test cricket batting averages, dividing the total scored in each innings by the total number of innings played for a test series it will not always work. Why?

Exercise 6.6.   The taxable annual income of nine families living in the village of Nether Region are £2720, £4389, £5212, £6421, £8275, £11 473, £12 430, £13 402, £124 742.

Which do you think gives the better measure of location – the median or the mean? What is the value of your preferred measure and why do you prefer it? Why do you criticize the other measure as an indicator of location or centrality?

Exercise 6.7. If you have a pocket calculator try using it to find the standard deviation of the following four observations using the method given on p. 79:

17 432 191, 17 435 204, 17 431 817, 17 444 012.

The answer correct to two decimal places is in fact 4916.33. If your pocket calculator gives you this answer without trouble using this method you have a good calculator. Test it further by trying to find the standard deviation of

17 432 191, 17 432 195, 17 432 198, 17 432 199.

Your answer should be 3.1125.

If you have trouble with this Exercise turn to page 279. Even if you got the right answers it is still worth looking there as an important point of principle is involved – one very relevant to the use of computers and pocket calculators.

Exercise 6.8. Remember the data you collected in Exercise 1.5? Consider it carefully and form any relevant five-number summaries and calculate means and standard deviations if you think these appropriate. What do the quantities you calculate tell you about characteristics of your data? Are there any surprises (e.g. unexpected skewness, greater variability than you expected? Is the mean very different from the median? If so, what does this imply? etc.)?

7 More about data summaries

The mode

We look first at data summaries in association with frequency displays like Tables 4.1 or 4.7. For such tables we sometimes use a measure of centrality or location called the *mode*.

For data in a frequency table, the mode is the value that occurs most frequently. In Table 4.1 – for computer printer breakdowns – the mode is zero, this being the most common number of breakdowns per day. In Table 4.7 it is 1, there being one call received in 14 of the observed one-minute intervals, more than any other number of calls per minute. A disadvantage of the mode is that it is not always unique. In Table 7.1 there are two modes, 1 and 3, each with a frequency of 32. Such a distribution is called *bi-modal*.

When there is a unique mode it is a useful quick descriptive statistic, but it is not readily associated with other measures of location and spread and so is less widely used.

Table 7.1. *Decayed teeth in 160 school children aged 11*

No. of decayed teeth	No. of children
0	29
1	32
2	26
3	32
4	21
5	8
6	6
7	4
8	1
10	1

The nuts and bolts of calculating means

Given raw data like that in Table 1.1 we all know how to calculate the mean – just add all the numbers and divide by the number of observations.

With frequency tables like 4.1, 4.7 and 7.1 we calculate the mean in essentially the same way though things may look a little different.

Example 7.1. In Table 7.1 the value 0 occurs 29 times, 1 occurs 32 times, 2 occurs 26 times and so on; thus to get the total we add together 29 zeros (easily done!), then 32 ones, i.e. 32 × 1, then 26 twos, i.e. 26 × 2. We continue adding these products of corresponding entries in each column of the table to form a *sum of products* and divide the final answer by the total number of observations, 160 in this example. Thus the mean number of decayed teeth per child, which it is convenient to denote by m, is given by

$$m = (0 \times 29 + 1 \times 32 + 2 \times 26 + 3 \times 32 + 4 \times 21 + \\ 5 \times 8 + 6 \times 6 + 7 \times 4 + 8 \times 1 + 10 \times 1)/160 \\ = 386/160 = 2.4$$

The mean is not necessarily, *and indeed generally is not*, an observable value (for decayed teeth these can take only integral values). This is a source of feeble statistical jokes based on statements like 'the average married couple has 2.3 children'. In this sense no individual couple is 'average'. The mean is *not* a typical observation. It is only 'typical' of the observations as a whole in the sense that it indicates centrality.

Since a table like 7.1 essentially gives all observations in order it is easy to obtain from it a five-number summary comprising lowest value, lower quartile, median, upper quartile, greatest value.

Exercise 7.1. Check that for the data in Table 7.1 the five-number summary is (0, 1, 2, 4, 10). The summary clearly shows the long tail to the right evident from the table itself.

Exercise 7.2. From the data in Table 7.1 prepare a graphical representation (similar in appearance to a histogram) to show the frequency of occurrence of each number of decayed teeth.

Your graph should help explain the relevance of the term 'skewness to the *right*' (p. 73).

Means and medians for grouped data

Example 7.2.   Another situation where we might like to calculate a mean or a median is exemplified by Table 3.1, p. 35. It is worth making a copy for reference. Suppose we have only this table and not the original data. Making reasonable assumptions we may still get a good approximation to the true mean. Let us assume all the observations in a group are at the mid-point of that group. Of course we know this is not really true; in practice it is likely some will be above and some below, but we hope that in the long run such differences will more or less cancel out. For the group 0–9 the mid-point is 4.5, for the group 10–19 it is 14.5 and so on. On this basis we can, as a working table for calculations, replace Table 3.1 by the pseudo-frequency Table 7.2. All we have done is replace the ranges in the first column by their mid-values.

In Table 7.2 we have omitted any rows corresponding to ten-minute intervals in Table 3.1 with no breakdowns recorded, since these contribute nothing to the mean. If you have a pocket calculator it is easy to add products of corresponding column entries for each row and divide by 90. This gives a mean value of 44.83, or 44.8 on rounding to one decimal place. We saw on page 76 that the true value for the Table 1.1 data was 44.9 – so we are not far off.

If you have not got a pocket calculator – or even if you have – you can save a little labour in calculation by coding the data. If you are interested we discuss this in Appendix A, p. 286; but it is by no means an essential procedure.

Petty fraud?

Time now to admit to a possible small fraud in Tables 3.1 and 7.2. We have talked of intervals 0–9, 10–19, 20–29 for convenience. It

Table 7.2. *Pseudo-frequency table*
for computer downtimes

Range mid-point	No. of occasions
4.5	24
14.5	22
24.5	13
34.5	7
44.5	6
54.5	1
84.5	2
104.5	2
124.5	4
144.5	3
174.5	1
184.5	1
234.5	1
244.5	2
334.5	1
Total	90

might be argued that there is no possibility of a 'zero' minute break-down and that therefore the first interval should be 1–9 in Table 3.1 and the range mid-point in Table 7.2 for this interval 5.0 rather than 4.5 (the other range mid-points remaining as given in that table). If we accept this, there is a slight difference in our calculated mean based on Table 7.2; it now becomes 45.0 to one decimal place.

Another argument that would suggest a slightly different mid-point is based on an assumption that recorded times are rounded to the nearest minute. Thus zero would refer to any breakdown lasting less than half a minute and 9 to any breakdown lasting between 8.5 and 9.5 minutes. The mid-point of the interval from 0 to 9.5 is 4.75 (4 minutes and 45 seconds). If however (as might happen in practice) breakdowns of less than 30 seconds are not recorded, we return to a situation where the precise breakdown range is from 0.5 to 9.5 minutes with mid-point 5. While one should take care about maintaining precision, one need not be too pernickety about minor details that have no important influence on conclusions. One should consider such details relative to the precision and accuracy of the data.

Standard deviations for frequency tables

To get the standard deviation (s.d.) for the Table 7.1 data, for example, first compute the sum of the squares of all the observed numbers of decayed teeth simply by squaring each number in the first column and multiplying it by the number of times each is observed; as given by the second column. We then subtract the square of the grand total divided by the number of observations. We got the grand total when we computed the mean. The next step, corresponding to step 4 on p. 79, is to divide this difference by the number of observations to obtain the variance. We take the square root to get the standard deviation.

Example 7.3.   For Table 7.1 the sum of squares is

$$0^2 \times 29 + 1^2 \times 32 + 2^2 \times 26 + 3^2 \times 32 + 4^2 \times 21 +$$
$$5^2 \times 8 + 6^2 \times 6 + 7^2 \times 4 + 8^2 \times 1 + 10^2 \times 1 = 1536.$$

We saw on p. 83, when calculating the mean for this data, that the total was 386. Thus the variance is

$$(1536 - \frac{386^2}{160})/160 = 3.78$$

and the s.d. is 1.94.

A similar procedure may be used to approximate the standard deviation of the Table 1.1 data if we only had the information given in Table 3.1, proceeding via Table 7.2 and treating each observation in a given range as though it were at the mid-point of that range.

Exercise 7.3.   Calculate the standard deviation of the downtimes in Table 1.1 and also an approximation to that standard deviation using the derived data presented in Table 7.2. Comment on the reason for any differences between the two results.

Exercise 7.4.   Could any of the data you collected in Exercise 1.5 be arranged in a frequency table? If so, calculate the means and standard deviations by the methods given in this chapter.

Means and meaning

Means are useful summary statistics, but they are sometimes over-used in trying to condense data.

Example 7.4. Table 7.3 is abridged from the Meteorological Office Monthly Weather Summaries for 1978 and also appears as part of Table 71 in the Penguin/Central Statistical Office publication *Facts in Focus* (1980).

It gives the *average* rainfall for the period 1941–70 for each month for (a) England and Wales, (b) Scotland and (c) Northern Ireland. Also recorded are the monthly figures for the year 1978 for these regions.

What messages do we get from this table? Let us look first at the totals. Each of the three regions appears to have had a total rainfall in 1978 differing little from the thirty-year average for 1941–70; but if we look at the monthly figures we see wide regional variations from the thirty-year average from month to month in 1978. Take December, for example; England and Wales had 174 mm., nearly double the thirty-year average of 90; Scotland is spot on the thirty-

Table 7.3. *Monthly rainfall (millimetres)*

Month	England, Wales		Scotland		N. Ireland	
	Average 1941–70	1978	Average 1941–70	1978	Average 1941–70	1978
Jan	86	111	137	158	104	134
Feb	65	86	104	104	75	74
Mar	59	78	92	166	70	113
Apr	58	52	90	52	68	32
May	67	47	91	40	73	31
Jun	61	70	92	69	79	57
Jul	73	89	112	90	93	68
Aug	90	71	129	110	103	80
Sep	83	54	137	177	107	112
Oct	83	19	149	99	107	54
Nov	97	54	142	198	102	117
Dec	90	174	156	156	114	205
Total	912	905	1431	1419	1095	1077

Source: Meteorological Office Monthly Weather Summaries, HMSO, 1978.

year average for that month; Ireland has not quite double the thirty-year average. One thing these figures cannot be taken to imply is that in December 1978 London necessarily had nearly double its average rainfall while Edinburgh had exactly its average.

Meaningless means

What do we mean by the average rainfall for, say, Scotland for the month of December? The table does not give the answer – we need further information. What in fact is recorded is the average for twenty-three weather stations operated by or on behalf of the Meteorological Office. They are chosen to be in some vague way *representative* of Scotland. Nine are in the North of Scotland (the Highlands and Islands), and seven each on the East Central and West Central southern sector of the country.

A similar situation holds for the other regions – England and Wales (an average for forty-six stations) and Northern Ireland (eleven stations). This type of regional mean is neither very useful nor very interesting. UK residents know the country is subject to sharp rainfall gradients. Rainfall is high in the Lake District of England, relatively low in the London area. In Scotland parts of Wester Ross have an annual rainfall exceeding 2000 mm. As one proceeds from south to north up the Great Glen from Fort William to Inverness, a distance of less than seventy miles, the annual average drops from 2000 mm. to less than 750 mm. Edinburgh has an annual average of 673 mm.; Glasgow 982 mm.

The fact that in December 1978 the average over selected recording stations in England and Wales was almost double the thirty-year average certainly hints that many, if not all, those stations recorded above average rainfall. The fact that Scotland was spot on average for that month certainly does not mean that all Scotland hit the average, not even that all twenty-three stations on which the average is based did so (remember, p. 83, that the mean need not be an observed value). Experience shows that rainfall patterns for south-west Scotland are often like those for Northern Ireland, so you might like to back a hunch that Glasgow, for example, had rainfall above average in December 1978! Some other areas, perhaps the east coast or the normally very wet Wester Ross area, may have been below average, bringing the overall Scottish figure down. But all this is supposition. Do more detailed figures confirm this?

The hard evidence

Table 7.4 gives the monthly rainfall (and the thirty-year averages) for the four main Scottish cities for each month in 1978. From it we immediately see that Glasgow had a below-average rainfall in December 1978, 93 mm., compared with the average of 104. So much for our guess! Aberdeen, Dundee and Edinburgh on the east coast were above average for that month.

Table 7.5 gives, for selected Scottish stations, the *December 1978* rainfall, together with this expressed as a percentage of the thirty-year average; 100 per cent means rainfall spot on average. Table 7.6 gives *annual totals* for 1978 for selected stations throughout the UK expressing them also as a percentage of the thirty-year average for each station. Comparing final columns in Tables 7.5 and 7.6 we see the percentage of average is more variable for the single month of December than it is for the whole year. This is a common phenomenon with data and reflects what is often referred to as statistical regularity; regularity implying that *short-term fluctuations often tend to cancel out over a longer period.*

Table 7.4. *Monthly rainfall in major Scottish cities, 1978 and thirty-year averages 1941–70*

City	Jan	Feb	Mar	Apr	May	Jun	Jul	Aug	Sep	Oct	Nov	Dec	Total
Aberdeen													
Aver.	80	57	51	48	70	58	83	86	68	82	88	76	847
1978	80	121	67	67	55	42	89	86	69	24	24	141	865
Dundee													
Aver.	64	48	45	45	65	57	76	83	68	65	70	69	755
1978	106	84	54	80	53	49	51	89	54	13	41	193	867
Edinb'gh													
Aver.	54	41	36	38	58	47	75	86	63	57	64	54	673
1978	58	75	53	49	24	49	69	72	63	13	50	99	674
Glasgow													
Aver.	94	71	61	61	68	61	74	91	101	103	93	104	982
1978	112	82	153	26	8	73	65	102	145	42	174	93	1075

Source: *Meteorological Office Monthly Weather Summaries*, HMSO, 1978.

Table 7.5.   *Rainfall at selected Scottish stations,*
            December 1978

Station	Rainfall Dec. 1978	Per cent of thirty-year average
Cape Wrath (Highland)	51	42
Wick (Highland)	62	74
Dyce (East)	160	213
Perth (East)	181	229
Edinburgh	99	189
Glasgow (West)	93	91
Eskdalemuir (West)	193	124

Source: *Meteorological Office Monthly Weather Summaries*, HMSO, 1978.

Some interpretations

One indication from the limited data in Table 7.5 is that the mean rainfall in December 1978 tended to be below average in the Highlands, above average on the east, and maybe near average in the west. This is borne out in broad terms by more detailed records (not reproduced here) which show that in the Highlands, rainfall ranged from 24 to 74 per cent of average in December 1978, in the east from average to 300 per cent of average and in the west from 72 to 234 per cent of average. So much for our guess, p. 88, that the east coast probably had it dry and the south-west above average!

Selecting useful tables

Tables 7.4 to 7.6 are much more informative than Table 7.3. To have figures for representative stations in typical rainfall areas is clearly more useful than figures averaged over widely different circumstances and based on largely irrelevant (from the weather viewpoint) political divisions.

Table 7.6 compares the annual 1978 rainfall pattern with the thirty-year average.

We could extend a table like this to include many more stations in England and Scotland or to cover also Wales and Northern Ireland. It is a somewhat exceptional year when any station has less than 50

Table 7.6. *Annual rainfall and percentage of average, 1978,
selected UK weather stations*

Station	Location	1978 Rainfall	Per cent of thirty-year average
Scotland			
Baltasound	Shetland	1144	100
Achnaschellach	Highland	2179	101
Nairn	Highland	642	105
Dyce	Grampian	877	106
Dundee	Tayside	867	115
Turnhouse	Lothian	699	99
Glasgow	Strathclyde	1055	107
Callender	Central	1596	106
Eskdalemuir	Dumfries	1438	95
England			
Newcastle	Tyne and Wear	742	116
York	Yorkshire	654	110
Cromer	Norfolk	646	102
Cambridge	Cambridgeshire	556	101
Derby	Derbyshire	672	102
Edgbaston	W. Midlands	729	94
Cheltenham	Gloucestershire	738	111
Kew	Greater London	598	100
Margate	Kent	443	77
Carlisle	Cumbria	739	85
Ringway	Manchester	756	92
Douglas	Isle of Man	1152	101

Source: Meteorological Office Monthly Weather Summaries, HMSO, 1978.

per cent or more than 150 per cent of its annual average rainfall, but as we have seen much wider fluctuations may occur for a single month. In 1978 all English and Scottish stations for which records are available were well within the above annual limits, indeed all but a few were between 75 and 125 per cent of the annual average. How different from the month of December!

Exercise 7.5.   Use Tables 7.5 or 7.6 to answer the following:
   (a) What is the thirty-year average rainfall for the month of December for Dyce in Scotland?
   (b) What is the thirty-year annual average rainfall for York?
   (c) Which had the higher thirty-year annual average rainfall, Edgbaston or Newcastle?

2 Graphics

8 Graphs, diagrams and data pictures

Table or graph?

A graph may be simply an alternative to a table, but it can be much more. The use, and abuse, of graphs is a subject in its own right. A fine account of all aspects of graphics, good and bad, is given by Tufte (1983) in *The Visual Display of Quantitative Information*.

We shall be concerned mainly with graphics in relation to numerical data (usually originating in tables). We do not discuss what is probably the most exciting development of the decade in graphical presentation, namely computer graphics. The advent of appropriate software, allied to new hardware, makes it possible to present dynamic graphs on a VDU – an ideal way to study the impact of changing conditions. It is impossible to do justice to this topic in anything short of a full-length book, so we confine our attention to graphs that may well be computer-generated – but which can also be produced by classical pen-and-ink techniques.

Data-based charts

We have already met, p. 41, the histogram for pictorial representation of data; the histogram is useful in showing the proportion (or actual number) of observations in certain ranges. Proportions can also be shown on the so-called *pie chart*. This is a circle divided into sectors or slices each with area proportional to the percentage with a specified characteristic.

Example 8.1.   In a large city 33 per cent of workers travel by bus, 10 per cent by train, 42 per cent by car or taxi, 2 per cent by motor cycle, 5 per cent by bicycle, and the remainder (8 per cent) walk. Figure 8.1 represents this information on a pie chart.

In this chart the angle of each sector is proportional to the percentage. Since there are 360 degrees (representing 100 per cent) in a complete circle, for the 42 per cent travelling by car or taxi the angle is 360 × (42/100) = 151.2. Note that combining bus with car and taxi percentages the total is 75, represented by three-quarters of the circle, or an angle of 270°.

It is advantageous, but not essential, to work clockwise (starting usually at twelve o'clock) with the sectors decreasing from largest to smallest. Each sector should be labelled either inside, as in Figure 8.1, or alternatively just the percentage might be put inside each sector with the label applying to its relevance (in our case, method

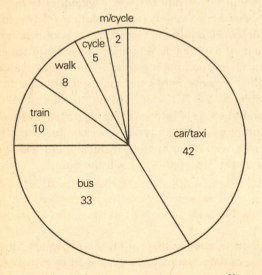

Figure 8.1. Pie chart showing proportions travelling to work in various ways.

of transport) written neatly outside the appropriate sector. If colours are available a gain in clarity is possible using a different colour for each sector.

An alternative way of representing this data is by a bar chart as in Figure 8.2.

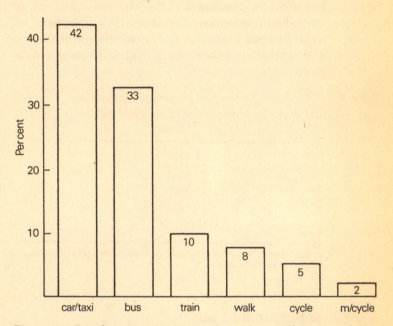

Figure 8.2. Bar chart representation of people travelling to work by various means.

Each bar is the same width, with variation in height indicating the percentages in each category. In effect equal proportions (or numbers) are represented by equal areas. In diagrams in two dimensions (e.g. those on a flat sheet of paper) area is the prime eye-catcher and the concept we instinctively compare; see Figure 8.7, p. 102, for an example of how one may be misled by overriding this principle. It is important to adhere to this 'area' concept also in histograms, and care is needed if intervals of different length are used in different portions of a frequency table. Histograms should always be constructed so that rectangles of equal area represent equal numbers. A complete study of histograms is complex and their use best discouraged except in simple cases.

Exercise 8.1. Calculate for each airport in Table 8.1 its passenger numbers as a percentage of the total passengers for all Australian State capital cities. Present this information on a pie chart and a bar diagram. On your chart and diagram give appropriate indications of total numbers as well as percentages.

Table 8.1. *Numbers of domestic passengers embarking and disembarking at Australian State capital airports (thousands), 1978–79*

Sydney	5539
Melbourne	4744
Brisbane	2283
Adelaide	1801
Perth	830
Hobart	456
Total	15653

Source: *Pocket Year Book, Australia,* Australian Bureau of Statistics, Canberra, Australia, 1981.

A more sophisticated pie

Example 8.2. Table 8.2 gives, for a motorway traffic census, the number of cars per hour passing a counting point during a twenty-four-hour survey.

Table 8.2. *Hourly traffic counts on a motorway*

Hour	00–01	01–02	02–03	03–04	04–05	05–06	06–07	07–08
Vehicles	532	273	204	168	143	281	862	1938
Hour	08–09	09–10	10–11	11–12	12–13	13–14	14–15	15–16
Vehicles	3294	5712	5913	6207	6714	5129	4327	5802
Hour	16–17	17–18	18–19	19–20	20–21	21–22	22–23	23–24
Vehicles	6043	6592	4836	4026	2795	2121	1645	997

Figure 8.3 consists essentially of a circular histogram for this data placed on a twenty-four-hour clock with 12 midnight at the top. This gives no more information than a conventional histogram, but our familiarity with 'circular clocks' aids interpretation and emphasizes that the trend for declining traffic as midnight approaches continues into the small hours. Another example of 'clock' representation of data is given by Moore (1980, p. 80).

In Figure 8.3 equal shaded areas no longer correspond to equal numbers because of the taper towards the centre. The degree of *penetration* of any wedge indicates the numbers it represents, and different penetrations enable us to compare hourly rates. This possible source of confusion and the complexity of the drawing may account for the rather limited use that has been made of this type of diagram.

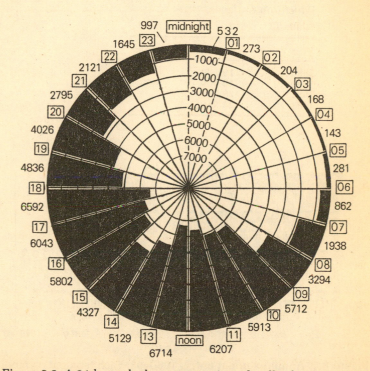

Figure 8.3. A 24-hour clock representation of traffic density.

Pictorigrams

A common pictorial representation of data is by the *pictorigram* or *picturegram* where a symbol is used to represent a specified number of units of the item of interest.

Example 8.3. Table 8.3 gives the number of full-time entrants to Scottish Colleges of Further Education in each of the years 1980–83. Figure 8.4 is a pictorigram of this data where each 'student' symbol represents 1000 students.

Table 8.3. *New entrants to Scottish Further Education Colleges, 1980–83*

Year	Number of Entrants
1980	19 520
1981	19 860
1982	25 130
1983	23 910

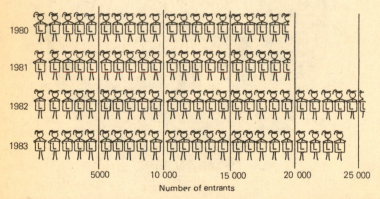

Figure 8.4. Annual student entry, 1980–83. Each 'student' symbol represents 1000 students.

Figure 8.4 shows entry fluctuations. We could of course also represent this data on a bar chart as in Figure 8.5. The only advantage of the symbolic diagram is that the use of the 'student' symbol immediately draws attention to the fact that the information is to do with people of a particular type.

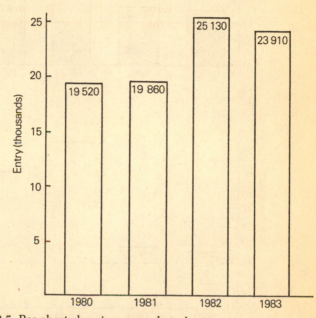

Figure 8.5. Bar chart showing annual student entry, 1980–83.

The totals entered in each bar in Figure 8.5 provide the full information included in Table 8.3. Thus the illustration serves the double purpose of giving a quick visual impression of the general nature of entry changes and full numerical information for those who want detail. We have written the numbers at approximately the same distance from the top of each bar so larger entry numbers appear higher on the diagram, a useful but by no means essential aid to comprehension. Sometimes each bar is shaded, but this is optional.

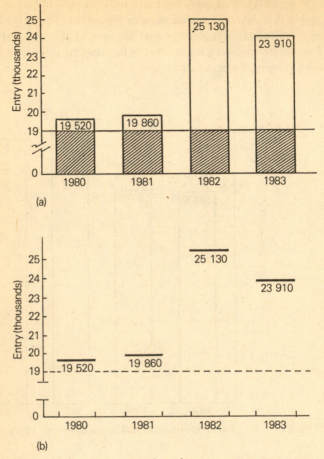

Figure 8.6. Rates of change in annual students' entries, 1980–83.

Chopped-off diagrams

To draw attention to special characteristics – for instance the annual changes in student entry – it is not uncommon to 'truncate' bar charts like Figure 8.5 by chopping off the lower portion.

Since, in Example 8.3, in none of the years 1980–83 does any entry fall below 19 000, we could show entries in excess of 19 000 as in Figure 8.6(a). Note the importance of the 'scale' at the left to draw

Figure 8.7. Watch your money grow in the Bluffshire Building Society.

attention to the cut-off at a 19 000 base line. The break below 19 000 also draws attention to the fact that the diagram does not use a scale that shows the *origin* or zero for the entry numbers. Graphs like this are common, but a much better way of presenting the same information is given in Figure 8.6(b), which demonstrates the advantages of simplicity.

Be careful interpreting such diagrams (especially if the cut-off at 19 000 is not made clear). Do not read Figures 8.6(a) or (b) as implying the 1982 entry is about seven times that of 1981!

Example 8.4. One trouble with chopped-off diagrams is that with a little distortion they become dangerous and effective propaganda weapons. We have all seen diagrams like Figure 8.7. I have chosen a fictitious name for the building society but the situation is all too familiar in advertising.

This diagram gives the impression that if you invest in the Premier Account your money will more than double in a year. The deception is brought about in several ways. The diagram shows in the un-shaded rectangle for each type of account only the interest earned *per cent*. The height differential between the two accounts is correct but by expanding in two dimensions (i.e. also in width) and thus increasing the area – the eye automatically quantifies area in making comparisons – the interest looks much better! Also the 'solid' bases (representing capital) differ in size in a meaningless way. One hundred pounds of capital is needed to produce £10.50 interest per annum in the Premier Account or £7 in the Standard Account.

Subtle use of words adds to the illusion; the statement '50 per cent more interest' is true in the sense that the rate of interest in the better account is one and a half times as good as in the standard account, but is there not a temptation to take '50 per cent more' to imply 50 per cent more interest than 7 per cent is 57 per cent! Some people are confused by the distinction between income and capital – especially if they 'invest' what was originally income (earnings for example) so that it assumes the role of capital. It is not your capital that is increasing, only the interest or 'income' portion, and the rate difference is $10.5 - 7 = 3.5$ per cent, not 50 per cent. The plain facts are that in one year £100 becomes £107 in one account and £110.50 in the other. You will be £3.50 better off per hundred pounds invested in the Premier Account at year end; a factor not to be sneezed at if you invest, say, £10 000, but the advertisement is designed to give dreams of more than doubling your money.

Many such graphical distortions are described by Tufte (1983, p. 57) using the 'lie factor', defined as

$$\text{lie factor} = \frac{\text{size of effect shown in graphic}}{\text{size of effect in data}}$$

In our example the size effect in data for capital plus income is 110.5/107 (a little more than *one*) whereas the effect shown on the graph by more than doubling the area is over *two*. Thus the lie factor is two or a little more.

Example 8.5.   Distorted or vague graphs are often used to make differences that are not really startling seem dramatic. Figure 8.8 is one that might be used to extol the virtue of the hire car firm; a very similar diagram appeared in a magazine sponsored by an official tourist authority. We use fictitious names. The diagram purports to show differences in charges per day for unlimited mileage for a similar car from each of five hirers. *Rent a Banger* looks a bargain at less than half the charge for *Luxury Limousines*. That is if you believe the units (unnamed) on the horizontal scale represent charges! But it does not say so. Somewhere hidden in the blurb you may discover that the figures represent charges *in pence* in excess of £30! In Figure 8.8 we are not told the units, only numerical values being given. The cautionary lesson from this example is to treat with contempt any diagram that does not show units, scales and origin, either on the graph itself or in a clear footnote.

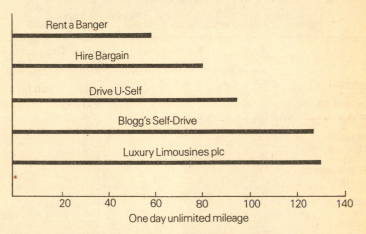

Figure 8.8. Relative hire charges for five car hire firms.

Graphs and relations

The most fruitful use of graphs is to demonstrate relationships between two quantities. The simplest form is the scatter diagram.

Example 8.6. Table 8.4 gives the number of days with significant rain (1 mm. or more) during the year 1978 at some centres through-out the UK and also the total annual rainfall at each of these. What evidence does the data provide on the relationship between these two quantities? In broad terms one would expect total annual rainfall to show some positive relationship with numbers of wet days.

Figure 8.9 shows a graph of this data with the number of wet days on the x axis and the total rainfall on the y axis. Note that we have used different symbols to indicate the four areas Southern England, East Anglia, North-east England and Western Scotland where the stations are situated. These areas are as described in the Meteorological Office Monthly Weather reports, though some may question the

Table 8.4.   *Number of wet days and annual rainfall, 1978*

(Area codes: S = South Coast, NE = North-east England, EA = East Anglia, WS = West Scotland.)

Station	Area Code	No. wet days (x)	Annual Total mm (y)
Alice Holt	S	118	778
Benmore	WS	200	2286
Bognor Regis	S	110	639
Boulmer	NE	134	854
Brodick Castle	WS	188	1851
Brooms Barn	EA	118	631
Clatteringshawe	WS	191	1874
Eastbourne	S	108	668
Glasgow Airport	WS	162	1074
Hayling Is	S	112	664
Hull	NE	139	725
Leeming	NE	122	649
Luton	EA	122	691
Low Etherley	NE	134	737
March	EA	118	660
Millport	WS	178	1095
Newcastle	NE	133	783
Pickering	NE	135	753
Rothamsted	EA	118	723
Rothesay	WS	186	1398
Shanklin	S	120	771
Silsoe	EA	111	542
Sloy	WS	196	2454
Southampton	S	114	744
Stirling	WS	145	1003
Threave	WS	144	1104
Woburn	EA	113	621
York	NE	123	654

Source: Meteorological Office Monthly Weather Summaries, HMSO, 1978.

grouping of parts of Hertfordshire and Bedfordshire under East Anglia. In the figure note the break in the x and y axes to indicate we do not start at zero.

The diagram shows a general trend; the greater the number of wet days, the higher the annual rainfall. In particular this trend accelerates sharply in areas with more than 180 rainy days. The

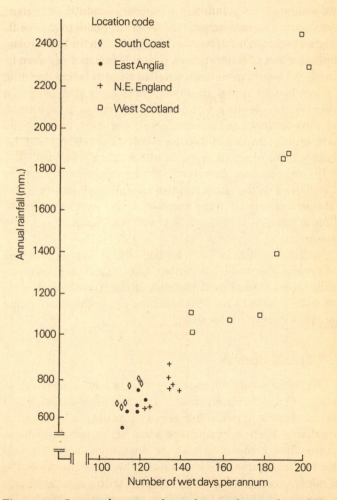

Figure 8.9. Scatter diagram of wet days and annual rainfall.

implication is that in areas where more than half the days in the year are rainy, then many of these days are really wet. The different symbols for different areas enable us to spot distinct regional differences. The points in the lower left of the graph (wet days less than 130 and rainfall less than 800 mm.) include most of the stations in East Anglia and the South-east (as well as two from North-east England). Generally speaking the points for East Anglia group to the right and marginally below those for Southern England, indicating a tendency for the same number of, or fewer, wet days to produce a rather higher total rainfall in Southern England than in East Anglia. The graph does not of course tell us how this higher daily average is achieved. We would need more detailed records before deciding if *most* rainy days are wetter, or if the extra is accounted for by just a few very wet days in the south. Records for centres in North-east England show little spread in numbers of wet days, many of the stations recording rain on 130–140 days with annual totals of similar magnitude to those recorded in the South on 120 or fewer wet days. Among the regions here examined, Western Scotland (we have already remarked on the sharp Scottish rainfall gradients on p. 88) shows the greatest spread in the numbers of wet days as well as in total rainfall. Wet days range from 144 to 200 and rainfall from 1003 to 2454 mm.

Incidentally, if the data in Table 8.4 had been arranged by regions rather than alphabetically by stations one might have seen the relationship more readily from the table itself. Alphabetical order makes it easier to select a particular station, e.g. Rothamsted, if one does not know its regional location.

Trend curves

Graphs like Figure 8.9 are called *scatter plots* or scatter diagrams. In many cases it is intuitively reasonable – indeed often desirable – to fit some sort of curve to indicate in broad terms the general trend or average behaviour pattern of points on a scatter diagram. A freehand curve may suffice. Figure 8.10 is a reproduction of Figure 8.9 with an added freehand curve. In a broad sense the curve illustrates the average rainfall we might expect in locations with a specified number of wet days x in the year. But beware, remember our data is only

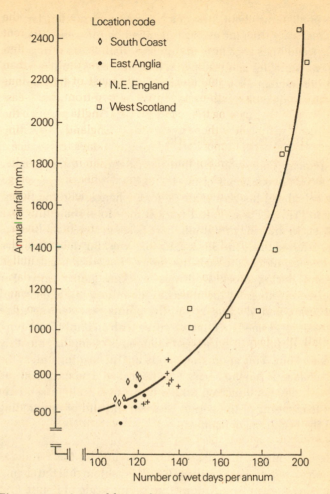

Figure 8.10. A trend line relating rainfall to number of wet days.

for a few selected stations from many throughout the country at which rainfall is recorded, and refers only to a particular year – so do not try and read too much into such a graph about more general rainfall patterns. Even if we confine our attention to the given year, and a named location with a known number of wet days, it is difficult to make predictions about how much the annual rainfall for that location may vary from the average specified by the trend line.

Simple trend lines are a form of summary statistic used in graphs relating two variables and occupy, in that context, a similar role to the mean or median for a single variable. Particular interest often attaches to trends with time.

Stock-market trends

In the *Financial Times* you will find every Saturday a graph giving for that week the behaviour of the FT Ordinary Share Index. The index is calculated hourly during Stock Exchange working hours, Monday to Friday. For a typical week it may look something like Figure 8.11. In drawing this graph there is some statistical licence. The days referred to are the Stock Exchange working day. The curve shown is continuous although the index changes are calculated hourly and during Stock Exchange working hours only. For example, if on Wednesday the index has the value 973.2 at noon and 976.8 at 1p.m. and 974.2 at 2p.m., the points representing these values are simply joined by a smooth curve with an implicit assumption that for all practical purposes the index is changing smoothly during each hour. This approximation is not misleading unless the Stock Exchange is having a very turbulent day. The circles at the end of each day (as indicated on the horizontal scale) essentially indicate telescoping of the period between the end of one trading day and the beginning of the next.

Example 8.7. Figure 8.11 shows the behaviour of the FT index over a typical trading week early in 1985. It is seldom that the change in a day is more than twenty points, so on the scale of Figure 8.11 there would be little advantage in joining the points by anything but a continuous curve. By so doing we would be discarding little information even if it were available. The closing value at the end of each day is clearly indicated by the circles. We discuss the basis of this index in Chapter 13, p. 177.

From Figure 8.11 it is clear that in the earlier part of the week there was a general upward trend apart from a slight hiccup on Tuesday. On Thursday the index behaved erratically and there was

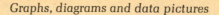

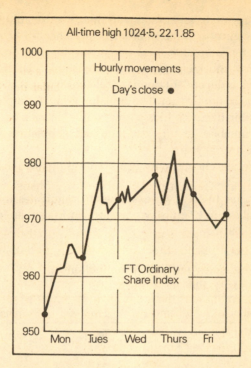

Figure 8.11. Changes in the FT Ordinary Share Index during one week.

a steady fall on Friday with a small improvement towards the close of trading.

This is a simple example of a *time series*.

Further examples of time series are legion – the familiar sales wall-chart is another. One might also be produced, for example, to represent demand for various fuels over several years. For comparative purposes it would be useful to plot the demand for the various fuels on one chart to make it easy to spot changes in demand. A difficulty here is choice of units. How does one compare consumption figures given in tons for coal, kilowatts for electricity, therms for gas, gallons (or metric tonnes) for oil? One possibility would be to compare total expenditures on each, but such figures could be misleading as consumption indicators because the prices of each fuel might change at different rates with time. For example, the cost of oil in many countries has risen dramatically since 1974 compared to other basic fuels. In 1986 there was a less dramatic drop in oil prices. This has knock-on effects in, for example, the electricity industry, which is dependent upon the relative amounts of oil, coal, nuclear and hydro production. The situation is much simpler when we are comparing like with like, e.g. car output in each of the EEC countries, or numbers of cars per thousand population in these countries over several years.

We conclude this chapter with two exercises on relationships.

Exercise 8.2.   For twenty-two examination candidates the marks obtained in Chemistry, Physics and French are given in Table 8.5.

Table 8.5. *Candidates' marks in examinations in Chemistry, Physics, French*

Candidate	Chemistry	Physics	French
1	73	68	48
2	82	71	72
3	69	60	74
4	29	31	53
5	45	41	42
6	68	51	33
7	89	81	72
8	23	16	49
9	84	67	56
10	51	48	59
11	71	72	44
12	60	56	51
13	43	41	59
14	69	55	81
15	43	41	61
16	49	51	29
17	83	76	51
18	74	79	43
19	77	70	71
20	16	10	49
21	53	51	16
22	62	56	64

Plot three scatter diagrams showing the relations between marks in (a) Chemistry and Physics, (b) Chemistry and French and (c) Physics and French. Comment on the main characteristics of each. What factors do you think may account for any differences (or similarities) in pattern?

Exercise 8.3. Table 8.6 gives monthly sales in thousands for two brands of raincoat, let us call them Wetshield (WS) and Damp-off (DO), over a two-year period. By plotting a suitable graph or graphs comment on the main features of the sales pattern for each brand, considering in particular any indication of changes in market share.

Table 8.6.   *Sales figures (thousands) for two types of raincoat*

	Jan	Feb	Mar	Apr	May	Jun	Jul	Aug	Sep	Oct	Nov	Dec
1985												
WS	43	21	9	6	2	3	7	11	29	53	51	49
DO	27	18	6	4	1	1	3	6	14	25	20	19
1986												
WS	44	23	15	7	2	3	8	10	24	31	36	35
DO	16	17	8	5	2	2	6	11	21	43	49	48

9 More sophisticated diagrams

Good and bad graphs

We look at more graphs, starting with a cautionary example.

Example 9.1. Table 9.1 shows the fixed capital expenditure in each of three UK industrial sectors in £ million in 1980, 1982 and 1984. It is divided into two parts, one giving the expenditure at actual prices and the other adjusted to 1980 prices. We defer discussion of adjusted prices to p. 116 and concentrate first on actual prices. Figure 9.1 is a graphical representation of the same data. Spend a few minutes looking at both tabular and graphical representations. Which do you find easier to interpret?

Which is the more informative about changing expenditure patterns over the three years? Do you prefer the table or graph for abstracting information like the following? Expenditure in the mineral products sector dropped by about 16 per cent between 1980 and

Table 9.1. *Capital expenditure in manufacturing industries (£million)*

Sector	Mineral products	Electrical engineering	Vehicles
Actual prices			
1980	447	565	863
1982	373	585	662
1984	444	855	823
Adjusted to 1980 prices			
1980	447	565	863
1982	318	508	570
1984	348	681	635

Source: *Monthly Digest of Statistics*, Central Statistical Office, July 1985.

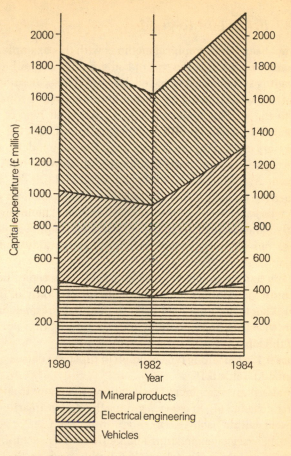

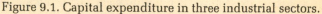

Figure 9.1. Capital expenditure in three industrial sectors.

1982 but recovered to almost the 1980 level by 1984. The electrical engineering sector showed a rise of nearly 50 per cent between 1982 and 1984.

Exercise 9.1.   Using Table 9.1 or Figure 9.1 (the choice is yours) discuss the major features of the expenditure patterns in each of the three sectors using the actual price data.

From bad to good

I have not been fair to graphical methods with this example, including it only because it is the sort of bad graphics seen all too often. The shading system is complicated. Despite clear scales it is hard to sort out just what is going on (certainly not without frequent references to the shading code to see just what each type of shading represents). Its main faults are: (i) complicated shading leads to unnecessary *clutter*; (ii) the joining up of the annual data points for each year gives a spurious impression of gradual change and detracts from comparisons at the three relevant dates; and (iii) the 'additive' pattern gives no definite base lines (except for the bottom [mineral products] sector) for year-by-year comparisons. The impression of gradual change is unlikely to be realistic since capital expenditure involves 'one-off' investment decisions rather than slow and gradual changes.

The key to clear graphics *based on a table* is to reproduce in the graph only the information in that table (or part only of the information if some does not lend itself to pictorial presentation), supplemented where appropriate by outside information not forming part of the table.

Figure 9.1 is the wrong type of graph to illustrate data such as that contained in Table 9.1!

Two alternative graphical presentations are given in Figure 9.2. The first, labelled (a), in essence groups the data primarily by years and shows within each year expenditure in each sector – mineral products, electrical engineering and vehicles. The second, labelled (b), groups primarily by sectors; then within each sector there is a breakdown by years.

Both of these graphs are simpler yet more informative than Figure 9.1. Which is to be preferred depends on our prime interest. If it is *overall* trends from year to year or comparing different sector patterns in the same year Figure 9.2(a) has much to commend it, but if we are interested in what happens to *individual* sectors from year to year then clearly Figure 9.2(b) is preferable as the 'annual' change within each sector is given by comparison of columns placed side by side. Putting the scale at both left and right is not essential, but useful if one has to scan across a fair width of diagram.

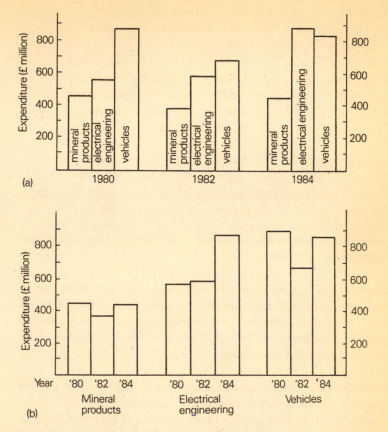

Figure 9.2. Capital expenditure in industry, 1980–2–4.

Derived tables and graphs

We could of course base graphs not directly on Table 9.1 but on data derived from it. For example, we might be interested in what percentage of the total expenditure for the three years in each given sector is spent in the individual years, as distinct from changes in the absolute amounts.

Table 9.2, based on Table 9.1, gives the percentages of the total

Table 9.2.   *Capital expenditure in manufacturing
industry. Percentage of sector total for three
years spent in each year*

Sector	Mineral products	Electrical engineering	Vehicles
Actual prices			
1980	35	28	37
1982	30	29	28
1984	35	43	35
Adjusted to 1980 prices			
1980	40	32	42
1982	29	29	28
1984	31	39	31

expenditure in each sector in each year both for actual prices and
adjusted to 1980 prices.

Exercise 9.2.   Using Table 9.1 check the percentages calculated in
Table 9.2. Each has been rounded to the nearest integral
value. This results in the percentages for one column not
adding to 100. Does this worry you? If so, why? If not, why
not? If in doubt see p. 280.

Exercise 9.3.   Produce graphs analogous to Figures 9.2(a) and (b)
for percentages in each category based on actual prices.
Study these graphs. Do you think any feature of the data
is highlighted more clearly by your graphs than it is in
Table 9.2?

In Tables 9.1 and 9.2 we also give expenditures *adjusted to 1980
prices*. These adjusted prices enable us to compare expenditure in
1980 with that in later years after making allowance for inflation.
The 1980 figures are the same in each part of Table 9.1. Why?

The adjustment is sometimes quite dramatic. For 1984 the electrical engineering figure drops from £855 to £681 million. The latter is
what expenditure in 1984 would have been at 1980 prices. Using
these adjusted prices for comparison gives a better indicator of the
relative volumes of capital work. For mineral products with actual

prices there is near equality of expenditure in 1980 and 1984, but the adjusted figures (£447 million in 1980 and £348 million in 1984) imply that appreciably less work involving capital expenditure was actually done in 1984. It is important in nearly all monetary comparisons to note whether or not inflation has been taken into account when making comparisons, otherwise one may draw incorrect conclusions.

Graphs and relations

In the previous chapter we highlighted the importance of graphs to illustrate relationships. They are helpful for comparing several relationships.

Example 9.2. Table 9.3 gives the number employed (in thousands) in each of three industrial sectors in June of each year from 1978 to 1983.

Table 9.3. *Number of employees in various industries (thousands)*

	1978	1979	1980	1981	1982	1983
Coal, oil, gas extraction	358	356	357	344	329	313
Electricity, gas, water supply	358	366	370	365	355	346
Chemical and man-made fibres	441	437	422	384	369	348

A graphical representation of this data is given in Figure 9.3. It shows certain clear time trends.

In all three sectors there has been a noticeable decline. This has been least marked in the electricity, gas and water distribution sector (where indeed numbers rose until 1980 before the decline commenced). The drop is most marked in the chemical and man-made fibres sector.

The drop might reflect declining output or sales in these sectors or increases in production per man. Before we could decide whether one or both of these factors operated we would need further infor-

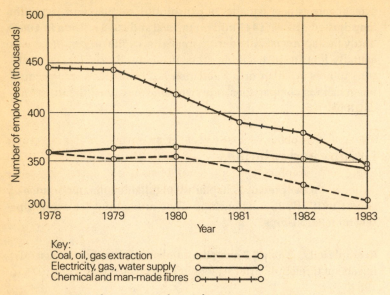

Figure 9.3. Employees in industrial sectors, 1978–83.

mation on output for the sectors. The picture might indeed be quite complex. The sectors are broad ones. A more detailed analysis (requiring more data!) might, for instance, indicate declining overall production of coal combined with higher production per man but a quite different pattern for water supply.

The importance of our limited data here is that it indicates patterns that may be of interest. The exact cause and effect mechanism is seldom clear from data alone, but by drawing attention to characteristics it stimulates research into their mechanisms. If we feel the matter is one of importance we must investigate further to find the *modus operandi*.

Note that in Figure 9.3 points corresponding to numbers in consecutive years are joined: a procedure we criticized in Figure 9.1! Here the situation is somewhat different. Although numbers are likely to change in quantum leaps in individual factories or plants, or as new factories or plants are established, the numbers are also affected by other factors such as resignations, new appointments, etc., occurring more or less randomly. The overall effect is that the implication of a more or less steady trend over the years is not in this case too misleading and indeed helps in showing the general pattern.

Box plots

On p. 73 we obtained a five-number summary for the computer breakdown times in Table 3.3. It was $(2, 9, 19, 41, 339)$. Tukey (1977) proposed a graphical representation of such a summary which he called a box plot. Figure 9.4 is a box plot of the five-number summary $(2, 9, 19, 41, 339)$.

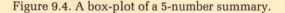

Figure 9.4. A box-plot of a 5-number summary.

On the horizontal scale the crosses correspond to the extreme values of 2 and 339. The narrow 'box' extends between the quartile values 9 and 41 and is partitioned at the median 19. Thus the box section covers the 'central' half of the observations. If there is symmetry in this section the median would partition the box in the middle; that it does not do so in this example indicates the skewness mentioned on p. 74. The crosses marking the extremes indicate the total range of observations and give some idea of the 'tail' spread in the top and bottom quarters of the ordered observations. We easily see what we mean by skewness (or a long tail) 'to the right'.

Example 9.3. For a single five-number summary it is debatable whether the box plot has any advantage over the summary itself; however it can be very useful if we wish to make a rapid assessment of the main differences between several five-number summaries. Suppose for example we have not only the summary for computer breakdowns in May 1984, but similar summaries for June, July, August and September. Suppose these are respectively (1, 11, 18, 49, 347), (4, 9, 21, 67, 304), (2, 12, 20, 61, 322), (7, 10, 18, 73, 297). Do these indicate any interesting variation in the pattern of breakdown times? Box plots of each on the same diagram help us answer. The plots are given in Figure 9.5.

We now see that the portion below the median partition is similar for all months. There are fluctuations in the maxima, but these reflect no clear pattern. One would reasonably expect maxima to be somewhat irregular as they may be associated with a major breakdown or routine servicing, forms of stoppage that are by their nature unpredictable in the time involved – except that it is likely to be lengthy. The top section of the box portion (M to Q_3) steadily increases in size as we move from May to September, indicating a tendency for a progressive increase in the length of breakdowns above, but not excessively far above, the median. Note that one piece of information not included in the five-number summary that might be of interest in relation to this pattern is the total number of breakdowns in each of the five months. A case may be made for a six-number summary when comparisons are required, giving as well as the standard set of five numbers an additional number N (the number of observations

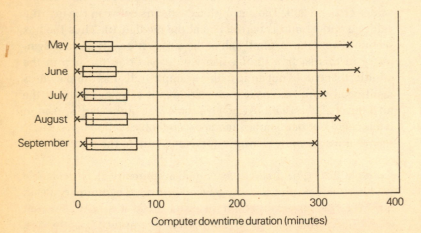

Figure 9.5. Box plot comparison of five 5-number summaries.

on which the summary is based). In practice where N is not too small it is likely that the size of N will have most effect on G and L, the greatest and least observations. Such a six-number summary might conveniently be written:

$$N:(L, Q_1, M, Q_3, G).$$

Exercise 9.4.   Samples of a hundred leaves are taken from each of five groups of bean plants; four of the groups (A to D) had each been sprayed with a different insecticide and the fifth group (E) was an unsprayed control. Counts were made of the number of aphids on each leaf. Five-number summaries for the counts for each group are given below. Draw box plots for the data and state any broad conclusions you might arrive at about the relative effectiveness of the insecticides.

Group A	(220, 397, 441, 552, 983)
Group B	(0, 2, 12, 81, 452)
Group C	(1, 1, 43, 62, 207)
Group D	(183, 222, 304, 321, 401)
Group E (control)	(250, 402, 429, 543, 1428)

Information maps

Maps are a commonly used pictorial aid. Outside atlases, probably the most familiar are the daily weather charts in newspapers. These show in compact form a variety of quantitative information on wind directions, temperatures, barometric pressure in the form of 'isobars' (curves linking places with a common atmospheric pressure) and sometimes rainfall as well.

At a more basic level, maps like the Ordnance Survey maps of the United Kingdom give a coded picture of the country. Types of vegetation are indicated by shading (green for forests, for example), heights being represented by contours, buildings of specific type by symbols such as a cross for a church (modified to indicate a steeple or spire as appropriate), or by letters (PO for post office). There is, too, a collection of symbols for roads, railways, canals, bridges and cuttings. Important as it is, a detailed discussion of this familiar example of representing data is outside the scope of this book.

Maps used in association with colour or shading can act as a useful diagrammatic aid to show characteristics of data associated with different geographic regions such as counties, states, etc.

Example 9.4. Table 9.4 gives the total numbers of cattle in each Australian State for the year 1979–80, the figures being based on returns prepared by the Australian Bureau of Statistics.

Table 9.4. *Numbers of cattle (thousands),*
         1979–80

New South Wales	6099
Victoria	4252
Queensland	10 332
South Australia	1067
Western Australia	2065
Tasmania	649
Northern Territory	1737

A simple map representation is obtained by shading each State on a map of Australia according to the scheme indicated on the diagram (Figure 9.6).

If colouring is available as an alternative to shading this is even clearer and pictorially more pleasing if we use deeper colours for greater numbers.

Although the map provides an easy rough-and-ready indication of the States in which the greatest number of cattle are to be found, it is really a confusing map. Does it really tell us what we want to know? Obviously the number of cattle will to some extent depend upon the size of each State. Thus if the density of cattle (the numbers per square kilometre) were the same for all States the larger the State the greater the total number and hence the darker the shading. To indicate simple totals per State we are better off with Table 9.4 or a bar chart based on it. We can make more sensible use of a map if we

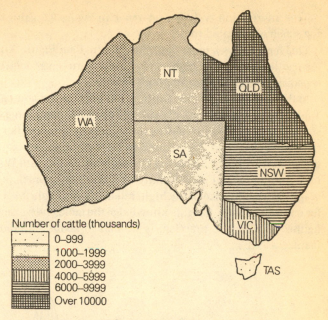

Figure 9.6. Map showing cattle numbers in Australian States.

want to compare the density of cattle, or numbers of cattle per unit area, in each State.

Using the numbers given for each State in Table 9.4 and given the area of each State (readily available from reference books) it is easy to calculate the number of cattle per square kilometre. This is given in Table 9.5.

Table 9.5. *Numbers of cattle per sq. km.*
         in Australia

New South Wales	7.6
Victoria	18.7
Queensland	6.0
South Australia	1.1
Western Australia	0.8
Tasmania	9.6
Northern Territory	1.3

This information is shown on a map in Figure 9.7 using the shading scheme indicated there.

This map shows a more definite 'pattern' than Figure 9.6. Clearly the cattle density is higher on the eastern coast of Australia, especially the south-east, than elsewhere.

In this rather simple case the map has a limitation compared with Table 9.5, as it indicates only *density ranges* rather than exact densities. It is however informative to anyone not very familiar with the relative positions of the Australian States. Unless one knows that the eastern seaboard States are Queensland, New South Wales, Victoria and the island of Tasmania one may not appreciate the geographical significance of the higher densities in Table 9.5. However, for one who already has this knowledge the table gives exact density figures. Shading, in practice, is limited to about six gradings per map.

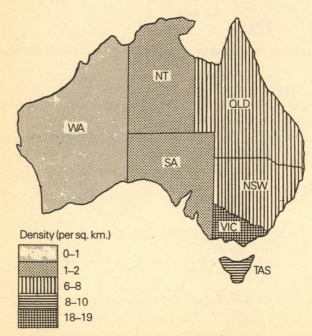

Figure 9.7. Cattle density per sq. km. in Australia.

We could do better. With a reasonably sized map we could simply present on it all the information of Tables 9.4 and 9.5 combined with the map's geographical information on relative location of States. Figure 9.8 is such a map. In each State the first number indicates the density information from Table 9.5 and the second number the totals from Table 9.4. We avoid much of the clutter inseparable from shading schemes.

Figure 9.8 is a concise and useful way of presenting data. It gives a lot of detail, but if only broad patterns are of interest the speed of assimilation is not so quick as it is with shading. There is, of course, an arbitrariness in averaging over a political area such as a country, state or county, but when data is presented only for such units this is often the best one can do. Here the effect is not so misleading as in our rainfall example in Chapter 7 (p. 88), for there the average was based on an *arbitrary* set of recording stations within each area.

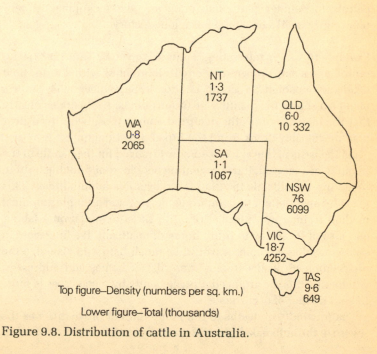

Figure 9.8. Distribution of cattle in Australia.

10 *Applied graphics*

Point plots on maps

Many a police operations room – in reality as well as in TV dramas – has a wall map of the area patrolled by the local force, spiked with pins of varied colours to indicate the scene of crimes of each type: perhaps red for sexual assaults, blue for robberies with violence, green for break-ins, etc. The dispersal of pins over an area gives a picture of crime distribution and may provide valuable clues about where to look for criminals or where to provide additional patrols to counter particular offences. The technique of 'pin-pointing' by marks on a map has a long history.

Example 10.1.   An interesting example is given by Tufte (1983) who reproduces a map prepared by one Dr John Snow with dots to show deaths from cholera in central London in September 1854. Snow's map also shows the position of water pumps. It illustrates clearly that the majority of deaths occurred among those who lived near (and presumably drank from) the Broad Street pump.

On the basis of this evidence Snow arranged for the handle of the pump to be removed, thus preventing people from drinking from it, so ending an epidemic that had taken over five hundred lives. This provides an excellent illustration of the power of a simple graphical method to interpret information with little computational labour and also of its ability to bring home dramatically the 'message' in data viewed as a whole. It would be much harder to visualize the distribution of deaths from a mere list of names and addresses, whether that list be arranged alphabetically by name or, as is more likely, in order of occurrence.

The proximity of deaths to the pump did not prove this was the source of the outbreak, but a water supply is often a source of infection and this was confirmed when removal of the handle appeared to end the outbreak.

Train scheduling

As early as 1885 E. J. Marey published a graphical method of train scheduling attributed to a French railway engineer. His example, one described by Tufte, concentrated on the busy Paris–Lyons route. We discuss a simplified example based on 1984–85 British Rail schedules.

Example 10.2. Figure 10.1 is a graph based on scheduled timings for eight main night trains – four in each direction – operating between London King's Cross and Edinburgh Waverley stations. On the horizontal axis time is plotted on the basis of a twenty-four-hour clock. The vertical axis represents the distance in miles, reading 'upward' from zero for London King's Cross to 393 for Edinburgh Waverley which is that distance from King's Cross by rail. We show on the left-hand scale not only the 100-mile distances but the actual position of 'stopping stations' for the trains (with one exception mentioned below). Lines ascending from left to right represent trains from London to Edinburgh and those descending from left to right represent southbound trains from Edinburgh to London.

The earliest of the four departures from London is 2025. This train is scheduled to arrive in Edinburgh at 0345. Note that the scheduled timing en route gives rise to an almost straight line with barely discernible changes in slope between pairs of stations. This implies that the train maintains an almost constant average speed between stations and the absence of any horizontal segments indicates that all scheduled stops are too short to show up on the chosen scale. The 2200 from King's Cross on the other hand has scheduled stops of 11 minutes at both York and Newcastle and these are represented by horizontal segments of length corresponding to the stopping time at each station, i.e. at York from 0108 to 0119 and at Newcastle from 0241 to 0252. The 'slope' of the line indicates the average speed between stations. We see that the 188-mile journey from London to York is completed by the 2200 train from King's Cross at 0108 imply-

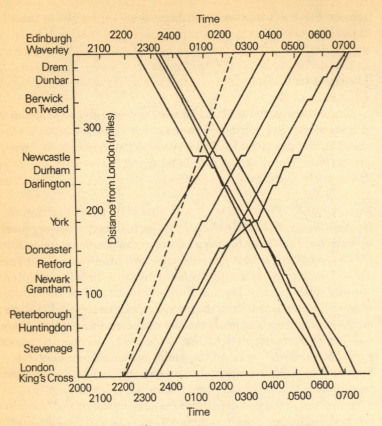

Figure 10.1. London–Edinburgh night sleeper schedules.

ing a journey time of three hours and eight minutes. Since 8 minutes is 8/60 or 2/15 of an hour we may express the journey time as three and two-fifteenth, or 3.13, hours. To get the average speed on this segment in *miles per hour* we divide the distance in *miles* by the time taken in hours; i.e.

$$\text{Average speed} = 188/3.13 = 60.1.$$

Note that we have expressed the average speed to only one decimal place. To introduce more decimal places would lead to spurious accuracy as the London–York distance is only given to the nearest mile and schedule timings to the nearest minute. Indeed, there is an additional source of error since we have rounded the time in hours to two decimal places. The final decimal '3' in the time recurs. If we express this value more exactly the average speed works out at 60 m.p.h. exactly.

A more straightforward way of working out average speed on a particular sector represented by a straight line on the graph is to note the distance travelled in one hour by a direct reading from the graph. In this example the train leaves London at 2200 hours and at 2300 hours it is 60 miles north of London just beyond Huntingdon. Thus the speed is 60 m.p.h.

Exercise 10.1.   What are the average speeds for: (i) the 2200 ex King's Cross between York and Newcastle; (ii) the 2300 ex King's Cross between Peterborough and Doncaster; and (iii) the 0010 ex Edinburgh between Edinburgh and York?

Note that the steeper the slope (upward for trains from London, downward for trains to London) on any sector, the faster the average speed over that sector. If the lines for two trains are parallel over a sector that implies they travel at the same average speed. Note that the lines for the 2025, 2200 and 2320 ex King's Cross are very nearly parallel for the whole journey, with minor fluctuations caused by different 'stopping' patterns at intermediate stations.

The point where lines for trains travelling in the same direction intersect is where the faster train (that indicated by the greater slope) overtakes the slower (that with the lesser slope). The cross of an up-sloping line with a down-sloping line is the point where trains travelling in opposite directions are scheduled to pass one another.

The above is a general rule. On p. 127 we mentioned there was one exception; this is due to the limitation of our graphical method. Between Doncaster and York the 2300 ex King's Cross appears to travel very slowly. This is indeed an artefact since we have plotted the data omitting one vital piece of information, namely that this train in fact takes a different and longer route between these two stations. It travels via Leeds, very nearly twice the length of the direct Doncaster–York route.

Also on the chart, for interest, we include a broken line (depart King's Cross 2200, arrive Edinburgh 0230), representing a time of 4.5 hours for the 393-mile journey. There is no such scheduled train at that time of night, but it corresponds to the journey time for the fastest scheduled trip on that route for any train, day or night – a time scheduled for the 1000 morning train ex King's Cross. Note the appreciably steeper slope for this very fast train.

The graph does not include some night trains that run over only part of the London–Edinburgh route, or certain weekend trains.

Control charts

Important uses of graphs occur in *quality-control procedures*: methods used to check whether goods are up to specification either during manufacture or at point of sale.

Easily understood diagrams can be used by foremen, plant operatives or clerical assistants with no special training in the statistical methods which form the background for the procedures.

A commonly used and simple method to check whether a manufacturing process is operating properly is to take samples at regular intervals and to measure and record certain characteristics. If the process is operating properly it is known what value approximately these characteristics should have. If, for any characteristic, the value strays too far from target it is an indication the process is not operating as it should. Just what is 'too far' can be calculated using statistical theory. Graphs enable the method to be used without having to know the theory.

Example 10.3.   A simple form of control chart is illustrated in Figure 10.2. It relates to a process that produces metal fittings each of which should weigh 1.5 gm.

We suppose that the amount of variability to be expected if the machine operates properly is known and is acceptable to manufacturer and customer. On this basis, a statistician then works out acceptable limits for total weights of samples of six fittings – ideally these should be exactly $6 \times 1.5 = 9.0$ gm. if each weighs 1.5 gm. – but the statistician may decree that any value between, say, 8.4 and

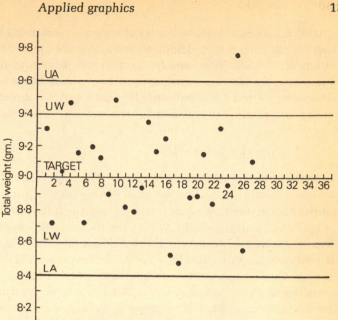

Figure 10.2. A control chart for weights of batches of metal fittings.

9.6 gm. is acceptable. Now, if the process is working satisfactorily successive samples of six will have a total weight that is sometimes just above 9 gm., sometimes just below 9 gm., without any very consistent pattern of surpluses over, or deficiencies below, 9 gm. Also, these totals must not exceed, or hover for successive samples, too near the acceptable limits of 8.4 and 9.6. If even one sample weighs less than 8.4 or more than 9.6 there is an indication something *might* be wrong – the machine consistently producing fittings above or below the acceptable weight.

It is well known to statisticians – indeed it is in essence a law of nature – that a sample may sometimes fall outside the range 8.4 to 9.6 without anything being wrong, but these values are chosen so that the odds are small – usually about 1 in 1000 – that this will happen if all is as it should be. In practice this means that if we stop the process whenever we get a total below 8.4 or above 9.6 we may have a false alarm, but it is unlikely. We should also be cautious even if no value falls outside these limits but we get several consecutive readings, say 9.55, 9.48 and 9.51, all just below the upper limit of 9.6 (or correspondingly several readings all just above 8.4). A rule often used is that the process is stopped if two consecutive readings lie between 8.4 and 8.6 or two lie between 9.4 and 9.6. Remember we stop for a single reading *below* 8.4 or *above* 9.6.

Practical details

Suppose a sample of six is taken every hour. The total weight of each may conveniently be recorded on a chart like Figure 10.2 (preferably drawn on graph paper), working from left to right equidistantly along the horizontal scale (labelled 1, 2, 3 . . .) for each successive sample. Thus the circles at vertical weight scale values 9.30, 8.72, 9.02, 9.47, 9.13, 8.72, etc., working from time 1 to the right represent successive readings. On the chart are 5 horizontal lines labelled *LA* for *lower action line* at a vertical scale reading of 8.4, *LW* for *lower warning line* at 8.6, *Target* at 9.0, *UW* for *upper warning line* at 9.4 and *UA* for *upper action line* at 9.6. If any reading falls below *LA* or above *UA* the process is immediately stopped and an investigation carried out. The nature of this investigation will depend upon the process. A first step might be to take a larger sample, or a series of further samples of six (immediately and not waiting a further hour) to see if our one sample is a freak. If the samples are consistently high or consistently low then the machine might be checked to see if it is in order; or, if the process involves making use of several materials, these may be checked for purity, correct composition, etc. For example, if the process is to make an alloy of lead and a light metal a heavy sample suggests too high a proportion of lead might be being used.

The process is also stopped and checks as above made if *two consecutive* readings fall between the lower warning line and the lower action line, or between the upper warning line and the upper action line.

In Figure 10.2 the observations have been numbered successively on the horizontal axis (if taken at hourly intervals these numbers represent sampling times in hours from an arbitrary zero). Thus in this example the process would be stopped after observation 18 (two consecutive readings below lower warning line) and again after observation 25, where the observation is above the upper action line.

Exercise 10.2.   In Figure 10.2 we show the first twenty-seven readings. Suppose the next twelve are 9.30, 8.52, 8.71, 8.43, 8.51, 9.02, 9.31, 8.35, 8.82, 9.33, 9.21, 9.74, when will the process next be stopped for checking? Would there be more than one stoppage between samples 27 and 39?

Simplicity

Control charts of the type just described are simple to use. They are easily modified to operate on a mean weight of samples of six instead of total weight, but the advantage of using total weight is one of simplicity. In neither case would the operator need to weigh six objects separately, all he need do is place all six on a balance and record one reading; but if he uses total rather than mean, he avoids the need to divide by six – a trivial operation on a pocket calculator – but one that is error prone. It is all too easy to hit a wrong key or to make a mistake in rounding off, e.g. to misquote 1.51666666 rounded to two decimal places as 1.56.

A more sophisticated type of quality control chart called the CUSUM chart makes use of cumulative evidence that things might be going out of control by combining evidence from a sequence of samples, but descriptions of this and other methods are outside the scope of this book. A brief description of CUSUM charts is given in the author's *Statistics in Action* (1977). A comprehensive account of the subject at a more advanced level is given by Wetherill (1977).

Flow diagrams

Finally, in our review of applied graphical procedures we present a technique not for direct presentation of data but for clear demonstration of logical sequences. We present it here because it often clarifies the analytical processes needed for collecting and using data, particularly in the preparation of computer programs to handle, edit and analyse data. The technique is one of increasing popularity and has recently found its way into newspaper advisory articles on such matters as how to invest £1000 to achieve objectives like capital growth or steady income in a variety of circumstances, e.g. whether or not an investor is a taxpayer, whether he is prepared to take risk, whether immediate access to capital is required in emergency – all factors which clearly influence investment policy. What is optimum for one investor may be unacceptable to another.

Example 10.4.　Even a simple procedure like buying a train ticket and boarding one's train requires several operations and decisions. Before buying a ticket one needs the facility to pay; the choice may be between cash or a credit card. To get cash one may have to visit a bank. Decisions must be made about the type of ticket to buy and this will be influenced by the nature of one's journey and the price of tickets. If one is returning by rail *within three months* a return ticket will normally be cheaper than two singles and if one returns *within one month* an Intercity Saver will be cheaper still. In other circumstances one should buy a single journey ticket. We exclude for the purposes of this illustration complexities introduced by special fare offers, e.g. day returns, differential peak day prices, senior citizen and young people's rail cards, etc. Having got the right ticket one boards the train. Figure 10.3 represents the procedure on a flow diagram. Three types of boxes are used in this diagram. *Oval boxes* pinpoint start and finish, *rectangular boxes* actions to be taken, and *diamonds* two-choice decision points. Paths through the flow diagram are indicated by lines with arrows to show direction. Other than the 'start' box, there must be one or more routes into any box. An action box also has one outward route and a decision box two outward routes, the one to be taken depending on which of two alternative decisions is made. All possible paths from the start through the system must eventually lead to a 'finish' or 'end' box (there may be more than one such box). With the above explanation Figure 10.3 becomes self-explanatory.

Example 10.5.　As our second example we give in Figure 10.4 a flow diagram for the logical steps that are required in a computer program to calculate the mean of a set of numbers. Don't panic. You need no detailed knowledge of computer programming to understand what

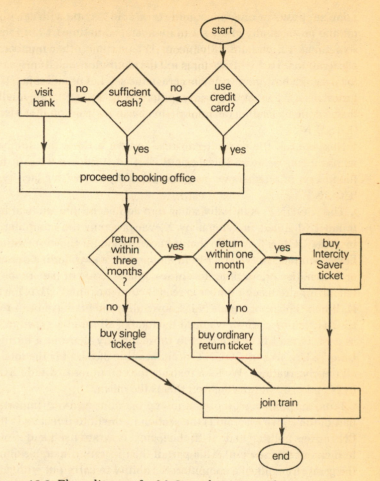

Figure 10.3. Flow diagram for Mr Jones buying a railway ticket.

we are doing. If you do know something about programming your home or office computer, you'll easily see what goes on. Preparation of a flow diagram for a simple example like this is almost an unnecessary luxury, but many of the 'bugs' that bedevil more complicated programs could be avoided if the programmer had first prepared a flow chart to confirm that all logical possibilities that might occur are dealt with.

We suppose our program is going to be able to cope with calculating the mean of any given set of numbers, sometimes 10 of them, sometimes 12, perhaps 23 or 34 or 122 or some other number of observations. To do this we must tell the computer each time we use the program how many numbers are in the set. Let us call this N (i.e. for each set we must tell the computer the value of N). Essentially, this is done by feeding the information by an instruction of the form 'READ N'.

Next we tell the computer to read, one at a time, the numbers whose mean we wish to calculate. So that it knows when it has the full set of numbers we program the computer with a facility to 'COUNT'.

The 'COUNT' is initially set at zero and each time we read in a number (denoted in general by X) we program the computer to increase COUNT by 1. So that it knows when all the observations have been read in (whether from an operator's keyboard, a cassette or from a disc or, for older machines, punch cards or paper tape or whatever) after each number is read it compares the COUNT with N. When the count equals N it knows all numbers have been read in. To calculate a mean we need the total of all numbers read in, so as each is read in it is added to those already there in a location called SUM. When COUNT = N the value of SUM is the total of all the observations. We then instruct the computer to divide SUM by N and print out the answer; this is the mean.

From the point of view of computer programming a very important part of the above diagram is the section in the dotted rectangle (the dotting has nothing to do with the logical diagram itself and is only to pick out this section). This part of the diagram illustrates one of the great strengths of a computer: the ability to carry out with great rapidity a series of simple operations a large number of times. In the dotted box each time we get to the end we return to the beginning until we have read all N observations. This sector is called a *loop*. In our example the COUNT facility is used as an indicator to tell the computer when it has been round the loop the requisite number of times. The last part of the loop is a diamond-shaped decision box, one route out being back to the start of the loop, the other escape from the loop.

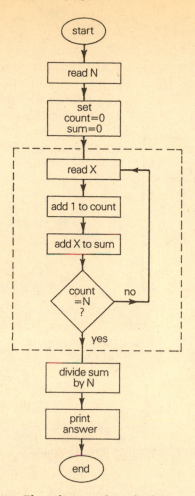

Figure 10.4. Flow diagram for calculating a mean.

The above method of calculating a mean is not ideal for a computer. Difficulties due to round-off or 'overflow' can occur if a great many very large numbers are involved. A better computer method is described in Appendix B if you are interested.

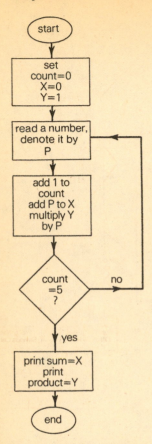

Figure 10.5. A computer programmer's flow diagram.

Exercise 10.3. Figure 10.5 is a flow diagram produced by somebody writing a computer program. Study it to determine what it does.

Example 10.6. Our final example of a flow diagram, Figure 10.6, is based on a common type of newspaper example and is self-explanatory. It gives advice on the best investment policy for a basic rate taxpayer to achieve certain objectives. The names of the financial institutions and investments are fictitious as real-life optimum

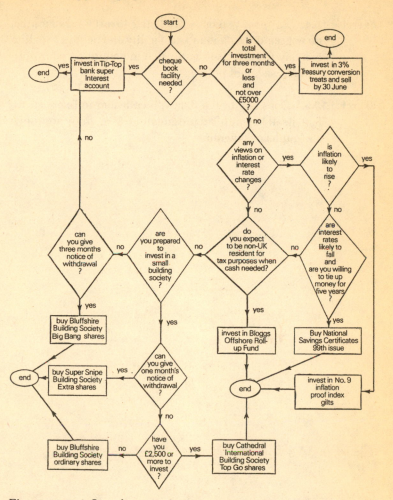

Figure 10.6. A flow diagram showing investment options.

investment procedures change rapidly (with changes in interest rates, inflation, etc.). Apart from the names the diagram closely parallels one appearing in the *Financial Times* in 1984. However, for technical reasons of newspaper production the symbols and layout used there were rather different.

Exercise 10.4.   Suppose you have £10 000 to invest for six months, do not require a chequebook facility and believe inflation is likely to rise. Use Figure 10.6 to determine your optimum investment policy.

Exercise 10.5.   Does any of the data you collected in Exercise 1.5 lend itself to graphical presentation? If so, draw appropriate graphs or diagrams.

3 Working with Numbers

11 *A feeling for numbers*

Ranks and gradings

Most numbers we have met so far have been measurements or counts. Numbers are also used to denote categories or ranks. Those associated with categories do not always have a meaningful order. For example, in Table 1.2 we listed in the third column the component causing each computer downtime. It may be convenient – particularly if the data is fed to a computer for processing – to allocate numbers to the various types of breakdown, e.g.

1 = printer

2 = tape reader

3 = CPU

etc.

This type of coding is common on maps. A town plan will often have prominent buildings or utilities numbered with a key at the foot, e.g.

1 = Cathedral

2 = Town hall

3 = Railway station

4 = Bus station

5 = Car park

6 = Public conveniences

There is no implication here of increasing or decreasing order of importance. To a potential rail traveller, 3 is more important than 4; to a visitor arriving by car, 5 may be the most important category.

In some categorizations, just as in measurements or counts or scores, order is important. Sometimes we have detailed measurements or scores, but we use these only to produce either a grouping into broad grades or a ranking in order of merit.

Example 11.1. In an examination candidates may be awarded marks on a percentage basis but the published results may only report a grade between A and E based on a scheme like that in Table 11.1.

Table 11.1.   *Relation between marks*
awarded and examination grades

Grade	Mark Range
A	over 80
B	70–80
C	55–69
D	45–54
E	under 45

Here, although A to E are letters they perform the role of 'grading numbers' in order 1 to 5, 1 being the top grade. We could equally well have written Grade 1, Grade 2, etc., in place of A, B, . . .

Placings in sporting events are essentially a *ranking* in order of total scores, finishing times, or whatever the appropriate measure of superiority is for the particular contest.

Example 11.2.   The leading scores in a club golf championship over 72 holes are: Smith 279, Jones 281, Green 283, Brown 285 and White 289. Clearly Smith is ranked (placed) first, Jones second, Green third and so on. These rankings would not have been altered if the actual scores had been Smith 280, Jones 283, Green 286, Brown 287 and

White 288. From the point of view of prize money it is the order, or ranking, only that matters.

Ranks may also be used to indicate an order of preference without an underlying exact numerical basis such as we had with the golf scores.

Example 11.3. In market research housewives may be asked to give a preference rating to five different brands of canned tomato soup rating them 1, 2, 3, 4, 5 from most to least favoured. This is not the same as allocating a score on a scale of, say, 0 to 5, where several brands may receive the same score. For example, a number of people may be asked to rate a new convenience food on this basis: 5 points if they consider it excellent, 4 if very good, 3 if fairly good, 2 if slightly disappointing, 1 if definitely disappointing and 0 if they consider it horrible.

In any such scheme there is an element of subjective judgement and differences in attitude towards using the scale. Some individuals may be reluctant to grade any product as either excellent or horrible whilst others quite happily use these extremes for any product they consider respectively either detectably above or below average.

Despite this, such grading schemes may produce remarkably clear-cut results either in the sense that nearly all people will agree the product is above average, or else there is a clear-cut division of opinion, perhaps some 75 per cent awarding high scores and the remaining 25 per cent low scores. This need not imply scoring inconsistency; it more likely reflects a clearly defined division in personal preferences. This sort of result is common for tastings of strongly flavoured foodstuffs. Some people like curry, others hate it.

A narrow range of possible scores is often best where there is dependence on personal preferences. Expression of preferences tends to become less meaningful if a wider scoring range is permitted; a range 0–20 is generally too wide for judgements with a high subjective element even when fairly detailed instructions are given, e.g. that the mark should be *about* 10 if one considers the product average, *about* 15 if good, 18 very good, 20 excellent, while *about* 5 means poor, 3 bad and 2 very bad. Respondents will differ in their attitudes towards marks between these 'indicators'. Some may avoid a mark of 12 or 13 feeling they should give a more positive indication of whether they really think it is good (justifying at least 14), or only just above average (justifying 11 only). The net result is often a wide spread of marks with a tendency to bunch near the yardsticks.

Numbers and their context

When used for comparisons, numbers have little meaning outside the context in which they are used. £20 is a poor weekly salary, but a good hourly rate of pay. It is a high price to pay for a pound of butter, but a stereo record player for £20 could be a bargain — or might have fallen off the back of a lorry!

There is a danger that people will put intuitive interpretations on scoring or mark scales even when a 'key' is given that flatly contradicts that interpretation. For example, if, in a guide to restaurants, you saw a mark of 9 out of 20 awarded to an eating house your immediate reaction may well be that it is below average. This is your likely feeling if you are one of the many people who regard 10 out of 20 (or 50 per cent) as about average. This outlook may well be a hangover from a school examination marking system where one is often expected to score a 50 per cent mark to pass. Yet the 1985 edition of *The Good Food Guide*, a prestigious guide to restaurants in the UK, awards each restaurant a mark out of 20 – actually recording these as 11/20, etc. – making it look like a school exercise mark. All marks actually awarded fall in a range from 8 to 16 inclusive. Now any establishment featured in the *Guide* is supposed to be well above average. The editor carefully explains in the introduction that the marks are to be interpreted in the following broad terms: a score of 8–9 implies restaurant activities are secondary to the main aims of the establishment (e.g. perhaps a pub that serves very acceptable food); 10–11 is for small competent restaurants, useful in the area, but without ambition to compete at the top level, 12–13 is for serious restaurants, 14–15 is for exceptional restaurants – worth going out of your way to find – and 16 is for restaurants where the chef shows consummate skill and whose influence is evident even outside his own business.

The Good Food Guide was happy to use this scoring method again in 1986 but gave a better description of how the system was meant to work.

Improving the system

The system is tolerable for those who read that information, but many users of the *Guide*, especially the occasional user, will not, and will instead put their own interpretation on the numbers. If a mark of 10/20 implies average to somebody, it seems likely that they will only regard a mark of 15 or above as really good. It seems therefore a pity that in awarding a mark *out of 20*, the *Guide* in fact used only the 8–16 part of the scale in a perfectly proper yet unconventional way, and that in doing so it placed any restaurant into only one of five categories, four of which have a two-mark range, i.e. 8–9, 10–11, etc., and the top one only the single mark of 16. People *might* have understood the system better if they had used the *equivalent* of a simple numbering system 1, 2, 3, 4, 5. We say *might* because that scheme has the inherent difficulty that it may be used in opposite senses – either as *scores* with a top score of 5 or as *gradings* with a highest grade of 1. (The Inner London Education Authority in assessing student performance awards CSE grades 1, 2, 3, 4 and 5 the respective scores 5, 4, 3, 2 and 1.) A guide book might be wiser to use a star system (1 to 5 stars); the accepted implication here is the more stars the better. One may also use, as *The Good Food Guide* once did, a pass and credit system topped by two special awards; one, a tureen, indicating all-round excellence and comfort with food at or above credit level, and the other, a pestle and mortar specifically for outstanding food and cooking.

Another well-known hotel guide gives percentage marks for standards of accommodation, with the brief introductory information that 50–69 implies Grade 2, 70–84 Grade 1 and 85–100 de luxe. One infers that an hotel awarded 78 has better amenities than one awarded 63, but I, and I suspect most users, find it hard to know what differences are implied between scores of 53, 55 and 56. The conventional percentages are here rather meaningless.

A recent example of trading on the mystique of percentages to make people think they were getting some sort of bargain was the legend on packets of a well-known brand of washing powder. It boldly proclaimed

> 6.2 kg. 33% MORE POWDER
> THAN ANY 4.65 kg PACK.

All true, but the appropriate comment is 'So what?' Clearly the intention was to imply there was some benefit pricewise in buying the larger pack. I never found out if there was, because 4.65 kg packs of this product were not marketed at the time!

Some traps with percentages

Be careful about manipulating percentages – particularly in dealing with percentage increases or decreases and in working out average percentages. Watch terminology also; do you know what an APR is or how it is calculated?

Example 11.4.   If your boss offers you either a 10 per cent salary cut this year then a 10 per cent salary rise next year to compensate, or alternatively a 10 per cent rise this year followed by a 10 per cent cut next year, does it matter which offer you take?

It certainly does. Suppose your salary is now £5000. If you take the first option you will get £4500 this year. Next year your 10 per cent rise will be 10 per cent of £4500, i.e. £450, bringing your total salary to £4950.

If you take the second option with the rise first, your salary this year will be £5500. The following year's 10 per cent cut amounts to £550, giving a second-year salary of £4950. You end up in both cases with the same second-year salary, but in the first year you will earn £1000 extra if you take the second option!

The important point here is that the *bases* on which you work out your rises and falls differ and the paths by which you arrive at the second-year salary of £4950 are not the same.

Example 11.5.   Consider a large company operating three factories. The percentages of employees in each factory owning cars are: 71% in factory A, 67% in factory B and 45% in factory C.

The   average   of   these   percentages   is   61,   that   is,

(71 + 67 + 45)/3 = 61. Is this the percentage of employees owning cars in all three plants?

The answer in general is no, unless all three plants have equal numbers of employees. *If they are not equal we must know how many are employed in each* (or at least the proportions of total employees in each).

Exercise 11.1. Suppose factory A has 200 employees, factory B has 1000 employees and factory C has 2000 employees. What are the numbers of car owners in each factory and the total number of car owners at all three factories?

The answers you should have got are factory A, 142 owners, factory B, 670 owners and factory C, 900 owners. Thus there are in all 142 + 670 + 900 = 1712 car owners out of a total of 3200 employees. So the percentage of car owners at all three plants is 100 × (1712/3200) = 53.5.

We can look at this another way. We require a *weighted mean* of the percentages. It is a generalization of the idea we first met in Example 7.1, p. 83, with grouped data. There, to calculate a mean we multiplied each observation by the number of times it occurred and added these products, dividing finally by the sum of the 'frequencies' or numbers of occurrences of each value. We may do something very similar in this case. We multiply the percentage for each factory by a 'weight' which in this case is the total number of employees and add the results for each factory, i.e.

$$(200 \times 71) + (1000 \times 67) + (2000 \times 45) = 171\ 200.$$

Next, we add the 'weights' (numbers of employees) i.e. 200 + 1000 + 2000 giving the total of 3200 as before. We divide 171 200 by 3200 to get the mean percentage 53.5 given above. The term *weighted mean* is used in any situation when observations (in this case, but not necessarily so in general, percentages) are multiplied by some appropriate quantity – the 'weight' (here number of employees) – before adding. In calculating a weighted mean, instead of dividing by the number of observations as in the simple case, we divide by the sum of the weights. Obviously, we may regard a simple mean of *n* quantities $x_1, x_2, \ldots, x_n$ as a special case of a weighted mean with all *n* weights equal to 1.

While we have framed the above argument for percentages, similar considerations apply to working out average proportions, or average parts per thousand or parts per million.

Exercise 11.2. Table 11.2 gives for each Australian State its area and population density, i.e. the average number of people per square kilometre. What is the average population density in Australia?

Table 11.2.   *Australian States, area and population density*

State or territory	Area (sq. km.)	Persons per sq. km.
New South Wales	801 600	6.34
Victoria	227 600	16.93
Queensland	1 727 200	1.27
South Australia	984 000	1.31
Western Australia	2 525 500	0.49
Tasmania	67 800	6.16
Northern Territory	1 346 200	0.31
Aus. Capital Terr.	2 400	92.63

Annual interest rates

What does it mean when a bank or building society says 'Our high-interest account pays interest at a rate of 9.00 per cent per annum – and interest is credited to your account daily so this is equivalent to an APR (annualized percentage rate) of 9.41 per cent'? Or your credit-card company says interest is charged at the rate of 2 per cent per month on any outstanding balance, equivalent to an APR of 26.8 per cent?

The idea of the APR is to tell you for a period of one year how much interest you would earn (or pay) on £100 invested (or borrowed) at a *stated rate of interest* credited (or debited) in a specified manner.

Example 11.6. Suppose you have £100 to invest for one year. You may invest it in the Bluffshire Building Society Gold Account which pays a rate of 10.5 per cent per annum credited annually, or you may invest it in the Brick and Mortar Society's Concrete Bunker Account paying interest at 10.3 per cent per annum with interest credited half-yearly.

If you choose Bluffshire, at the end of the year your £100 will grow to £110.50. If you choose Brick and Mortar, at the end of six months your £100 will have added to it one half of £10.30, i.e. £5.15, i.e. half the interest implied by the annual rate. However, in the second half-year you receive interest not only on your one hundred pounds, but *also* on the extra £5.15.

The interest for a half-year on £100 is again £5.15, and the 'extra' interest due on £5.15 is £$(5.15/100) \times 5.15 = 5.15^2/100 = £0.27$ (to 2 decimal places).

Thus in the Brick and Mortar Building Society the interest received at the end of one year consists of two payments of £5.15 each on £100 for six months plus an additional payment of 27p interest for the second six months on the interest of £5.15 earned after the first six months. Thus for the year the total interest is £10.57. So the second investment is the better by 7p.

This calculation can be telescoped. An interest rate of 5.15 for a specified period (here a half-year) implies that £1.00 will grow to £1.0515 in that period. This gives the growth factor *per pound* for each period. At the start of the second six months our £1 has become £1.0515 and in each succeeding six-month period it grows by this same factor, thus after two periods it has grown to £$(1.0515)^2$. This equals £1.1057 to 4 decimal places. Thus £100 would grow to £110.57. The APR is 10.57 per cent.

Example 11.7. The same principle can be applied to credit-card repayments. If a credit-card company charges interest at 2 per cent *per month* then after one month a debt of £1 becomes £1.02. In each succeeding month it grows by the same factor, becoming £$(1.02)^2$ after 2 months, £$(1.02)^3$ after 3 months and so on. Thus after 12 months a debt of £1 grows to £$(1.02)^{12} = 1.268$ to 3 decimal places. Thus £100 grows to £126.8, equivalent to an APR of 26.8 per cent.

Exercise 11.3. It is instructive to note how APR changes for different monthly interest rates. Complete Table 11.3.

Table 11.3.   *Monthly interest rates and APR*

Monthly interest rate	APR
1%	?
1.25%	?
1.5%	?
1.75%	?
2%	26.8%
2.5%	?
3%	?
4%	60.1%

Example 11.8.   The same idea extends to an interest rate of, say, 8.8 per cent per annum credited daily. This means the daily interest per £100 is £8.8/365 = £0.0241096 pounds. For £1.00 it is 1/100 of this, i.e. £0.000241096. In other words in one day £1 grows to £1.000241096, in two days it grows to £$(1.000241096)^2$, in three days to £$(1.000241096)^3$ and finally in 365 days, or one year, to £$(1.000241096)^{365}$. This is easily evaluated on a pocket calculator with a y^x facility, or else using logarithms, and the answer is £1.0920. Thus in one year, if interest is credited daily at a rate corresponding to 8.8 per cent per annum, each pound grows by £0.0920 pounds or £100 grows by £9.20 so the APR is 9.20 per cent. Note that we expressed the daily interest rate to 9 decimal places. This is important when we raise a number near unity to a high power. Had we rounded off to five decimal places using 1.00024^{365} we would have concluded our APR was 9.15 per cent rather than 9.20 per cent.

Exercise 11.4.   Two high-interest bank accounts advertise that they currently pay interest at the following 'per annum' rates:

Account A: 9.3 per cent, interest credited monthly.

Account B: 9.2 per cent, interest credited daily.

If I have a sum of money I wish to invest now and leave for 12 months, which will give the better rate of return if the advertised interest rates remain the same?

With certain types of account – especially those associated with the so-called 'money market' – the advertised interest rate on which daily or monthly calculations are made changes every few days and there will be a consequential change in the APR. A quoted annual rate at which interest is calculated reflects the real base for *current* interest calculations; the APR tells what would happen over a twelve-month period if the interest rate remained at its *current* level for that time – assuming you left your capital intact.

You may have seen the term CAR (compound annual rate). It is rather like APR but takes into account tax deducted at source.

Flat and true interest rates

The exact interest payable on loans causes much confusion, especially when loans are paid back by instalments, perhaps half-yearly, or quarterly, or monthly.

Example 11.9. To take a very simple example, suppose a man borrows £200 and agrees to pay interest at a true rate of 20 per cent per annum, and the loan plus interest is to be paid in two equal half-yearly instalments with the understanding that immediately prior to each payment interest at the above rate is charged to his account for the balance outstanding over the previous six months. What should each instalment be?

It requires a little algebra to work this out, but if we do this the answer comes out as £115.24. Having got the answer it is easily verified. Since 20 per cent per annum is equivalent to 10 per cent per half-year, at the end of six months interest of £20 is due on the full amount outstanding of £200, making the total debt £220. If £115.24 is paid there remains a debt of £220 − £115.24 = £104.76. Just before the second and final payment six months later, interest of £10.48 (to the nearest penny) is due on this, making a total of £115.24, thus verifying our assertion that each instalment should be £115.24. For the loan of £200 the total repayment has been £230.48, with an interest payment of £30.48, a percentage of 15.24. This percentage is often referred to as the *flat* rate per annum. It is the rate one would pay if the whole amount had been borrowed for one year and repayment in full made after that time. It is appreciably less than the *applied* rate of 20 per cent since it ignores the fact that half the debt was owed for only six months. Before tighter controls were enforced by law some years ago in the UK, often only the flat rate was quoted in loan advertisements. It however distorts the true picture with instalment repayment and now any authorized lender must quote an APR calculated by approved methods, which are understandably complex as they have to take into account the precise rules as to when interest is charged on the loan, any charges made for arranging the loan and the rate at which repayments are made. We will not describe the details of the complicated APR calculations needed for loans such as mortgages.

Per annum

While flat or true rates are most often quoted *per annum* note that other bases are used. We have already mentioned that credit-card companies often quote a *per month* interest rate – in the UK currently of the order of 1.5 to 2 per cent. Unscrupulous moneylenders sometimes quote a rate which would be tolerable as a per annum rate without making it clear it is a rate per week. A rate of 20 per cent per week means that a debt of £1 becomes a debt of £$(1.20)^{52}$ = £13 104.63 if left for one year. This means that £100 borrowed for one year would require a repayment of £1 310 463. Deduct the capital of £100, and the interest due amounts to £1 310 363, so the APR is 1 310 363 per cent! Before recent changes in legislation, at least one UK moneylender was making loans on this basis. It is to be hoped most borrowers took only short-term loans from him!

Exercise 11.5.   Make the calculations to complete Table 11.4.

A feeling for calculated numbers

We have mentioned several times the very real danger of getting an incorrect answer with a pocket calculator simply by hitting the wrong key. Equally, computers will produce meaningless answers if incorrectly programmed or if errors are made in feeding in data.

    Spotting serious errors is often little more than applying common-

Table 11.4.   *Weekly interest rates and APR*

Weekly interest rate	APR
1%	?
2%	?
5%	?
10%	?
20%	1 310 363%

sense checks. In calculating a mean for example, the mean always lies between the greatest and least observations. Thus if all observations are two-digit integers a mean of 103 is obviously incorrect. Also a sum of squares of deviations from the mean, or the mean of that sum of squares, the variance, must always be positive, since squares of numbers – positive or negative – are always positive; thus their sum must be positive. The only exception is if we square a set of zeros – then their squares are all zero. A negative sum of squares of deviations is clearly an indication that something is wrong.

Orders of magnitude

In more sophisticated calculations it is always worth getting an idea of the order of magnitude you expect in an answer. In commercial calculations these are often little more than using one's common sense. If a commodity costs £20 per ton and you are interested in the price per pound, then if you know there are 2240 lb in a ton (or 1000 kg in a metric tonne) it is obvious that the price per pound is a little less than one penny (or the price per kilogram is 2p). Our reasoning here is simply that £20 is 2000 pence, the same *order of magnitude* as the number of pounds (weight) in one ton. In some calculations we may have little idea of the answer before we start, but a look at the figures indicates what to expect.

Example 11.10.   Suppose we wish to calculate:

$$\frac{17 \times 16 \times 15 \times 14}{36 \times 35 \times 34 \times 33}.$$

Would you be surprised if you got as answer 0.657? You should be? Why? Look at the corresponding terms (factors) above and below in the expression; 17 divided by 36 is a little less than one half, similarly 16/35 is a little less than 1/2, so are 15/34 and 14/33. Thus the whole expression is less than

$$\frac{1}{2} \times \frac{1}{2} \times \frac{1}{2} \times \frac{1}{2}$$

i.e. less than 1/16 = 0.0625.

Exercise 11.6.   Calculate the value of the quotient in Example 11.10 to 4 decimal places.

Order of calculation

We have already pointed out in Exercise 6.6, p. 80, that computers or pocket calculators can run into difficulties with very large numbers leading at best to round-off errors and at worst to a failure to cope with the computation at all. Very often the order in which operations are carried out is important. If the final answer is moderate in size one should try and avoid working to the answer via operations such as subtraction of two large numbers that are nearly equal, or division of two large numbers that have a relatively small quotient.

Example 11.11.   If one wishes to calculate

$$\frac{450 \times 449 \times 448 \times 447 \times 446 \times 445 \times 444 \times 443 \times 442 \times 441 \times 440}{461 \times 460 \times 459 \times 458 \times 457 \times 456 \times 455 \times 454 \times 453 \times 452 \times 451}$$

using similar arguments to those in Example 11.10 it is obvious that the answer is just a little less than one. Now try multiplying together all the numbers in the top row (the numerator). Depending on the type of calculator you have it will either rebel, because the number is too big for it to handle, or give you a greatly rounded-off version of the product. Now do the same for the denominator. The result will be much the same. If you divide the two results the answer will depend very much on your particular calculator. Mine gives the answer 0.7644 to four decimal places and this is correct. A safer way, however, to do the computation is by successive divisions and multiplications working from left to right, i.e. first divide 450 by 461, then multiply by 449 and divide by 460, then multiply by 448 and divide by 459 and so on, finally multiplying by 440 and dividing by 451.

Proceeding in this way, at no stage will the entry on the calculator be more than 461 or less than the final answer of 0.7644.

Here's a hint. When keying into a calculator it helps to cover up unwanted parts of the fraction with cards as in Figure 11.1. The cards can be slipped along as you complete each phase of the calculation. This device is often useful when keying data from tables, etc., into a calculator or computer.

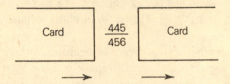

Figure 11.1. Using cards to pick out entries.

Difficulties may also occur with a pocket calculator if attempts are made to take the product of a very small and a very large number.

Exercise 11.7. Try the following calculation on your pocket calculator. Multiply 1 743 298 710 by 0.000 000 000 573 625 159 2.

If you are unhappy about the answer you get, turn to p. 282.

12 Combining numbers

Combination of measurements or scores

If we weigh five objects separately their total weight is clearly obtained by adding the weights of each *providing all are measured in the same units*, e.g. all in grams. Clearly if one object was known to weigh 6 kg. and another 112 gm. we would not record their total weight as 112 + 6 = 118 anything, but convert to common units – either 6 kg. = 6000 gm. or 112 gm. = 0.112 kg., giving a total weight of 6112 gm. or 6.112 kg. This is so obvious it hardly needs saying.

It is often less clear whether any sensible meaning can be attached to the addition of sets of numbers. Complex scoring systems are used for events like a decathlon in sporting contests; here points are awarded in a way designed to reflect standards of achievement in very different fields of endeavour.

Some thought and care is needed in adding examination marks in different subjects to decide – on the basis of an overall total – the award of a bursary or prize. The problems that arise there are also found in other situations; for example, in psychological tests different scores are often awarded for tests designed primarily to detect particular abilities. Psychologists have long been aware that in comparing performances in different tests the 'raw' scores in each may not be comparable. For these reasons alone educationalists and psychologists often adopt a procedure called standardization of scores. There is no universally correct method of standardization, but we illustrate the basic principles with an educational example.

Example 12.1. Table 12.1 gives the percentage marks scored by each of forty candidates in examinations in English and Mathematics. Suppose three prizes or scholarships are to be awarded and the object is to select the candidates best

Table 12.1. *Examination percentage marks in Mathematics and English*

Candidate	Mathematics	English	Total
1	54	57	111
2	55	61	116
3	64	59	123
4	19	27	46
5	14	25	39
6	11	32	43
7	56	51	107
8	56	54	110
9	89	72	161
10	59	61	120
11	96	70	166
12	23	24	47
13	87	72	159
14	31	29	60
15	42	44	86
16	7	22	29
17	53	51	104
18	54	53	107
19	54	48	102
20	18	22	40
21	40	43	83
22	57	61	118
23	43	48	91
24	44	50	94
25	44	43	87
26	21	22	43
27	84	76	160
28	47	43	90
29	48	51	99
30	50	47	97
31	51	54	105
32	52	55	107
33	52	47	99
34	32	37	69
35	73	71	144
36	78	64	142
37	36	44	80
38	81	77	158
39	81	71	152
40	71	63	134

suited to receive them. We further suppose the ordering of the first three is important as the awards are worth respectively £200, £100 and £50. The most obvious procedure would be to total the marks in the two subjects and award the prizes to the candidates with the three highest totals. But is this fair? If not, can we devise a fairer way of doing things?

To pinpoint interesting features of the marks for each subject we first use this data as an exercise on earlier ideas.

Exercise 12.1.   Prepare separate stem and leaf diagrams for the marks in each subject and also obtain five-number summaries. Draw adjacent box plots for the two data sets. What are the main differences you notice?

The five-number summaries are:

For Mathematics: (7, 38, 52, 61.5, 96)
For English: (22, 43, 51, 61, 77).

The medians are very similar, the quartiles not strikingly different. However, the extreme values, greatest and least, imply a considerably greater range for Mathematics marks than for English. The mark distributions are fairly symmetric. Anyone familiar with examinations marked on a percentage scale will be little surprised by these findings. It is quite common for bad candidates in Mathematics to score virtually no marks, for perhaps they will be able to make only feeble attempts at one or two questions and quite unable even to start others. There are clearly defined correct answers to most mathematical questions and an examiner will normally give full marks for a question so answered. Thus a good candidate who gives near-perfect answers to all questions may expect a very high percentage mark.

Assessing performance in most subjects other than Mathematics involves a higher subjective element, subjectivity steadily increasing as we move from the core science subjects through the social sciences to arts topics. The result is that in non-mathematical examinations, even weak candidates usually score a few marks on nearly every question, so a mark much lower than about twenty is unusual. At the other end of the scale there is often no clearly defined perfect answer to a question such as 'State, giving reasons, which of Charles Dickens's novels you believe to present the most convincing condemnation of the social conditions of his era'.

Consequently, it is seldom that a total mark much in excess of 80 per cent is awarded to any candidate in English. Indeed, most other subjects, for example, Physics, Chemistry, French, Geography, History, Economics, very seldom produce the extremes of marks we find in many Mathematics examinations.

This casts doubt upon the desirability of deciding prizewinners by adding the marks in different subjects and awarding the prizes to those with the highest marks. The unfairness of this method is compounded in a situation where candidates may choose any three out of a group of, say, eight subjects and the marks are added for each candidate's chosen three. Clearly if what we have said holds, good candidates who include Mathematics in their selected three have an unfair advantage, since a good mathematician has the edge on a candidate with a good performance in three subjects not including Mathematics.

Exercise 12.2. Using the total marks in the last column of Table 12.1, pick out the top eight performers in order. If three prizes are available, which candidates would receive them if they are awarded on the basis of best total mark?

The top scoring candidates (with their total mark in brackets) are: 1, Number 11 (166); 2, Number 9 (161); 3, Number 27 (160); 4, Number 13 (159); 5, Number 38 (158); 6, Number 39 (152); 7, Number 35 (144); 8, Number 36 (142).

Candidate Number 11 got the very high top mark of ninety-six in Mathematics and an acceptable seventy in English. However, if we look at the English marks (or better still at the stem and leaf diagram prepared in Exercise 12.1) we see that six candidates got higher marks in English. Now, check in the same way from the table, or your stem and leaf display, and you will find that candidate Number 9, who comes second on a total basis, is second in Mathematics and equal third in English, while candidate Number 27 who came third on a total basis was fourth in Mathematics and second in English. Now, if three prizes are different in value so that order really matters, should not consistency of performance be taken into account? Is not a candidate who is in the top three or four in each subject perhaps more worthy than one who finishes first in one subject and seventh in another?

This question has no clear-cut correct answer. Certainly a mark of ninety-six in Mathematics is seven marks better than that obtained by any other person in that subject, whereas the candidate who had this mark, although only seventh in order of merit in English, still had a mark only seven below the top mark in English.

If we take another approach and rank candidates in order of merit in each subject and then add their two ranks we get a substantially different ordering.

Exercise 12.3.   Use your stem and leaf displays to calculate the rank in each subject for each of the top eight candidates as ranked by marks in that subject. Where two candidates have scored the same mark in a subject they should be given a 'half rank', e.g. if two candidates score seventy and there are only three higher marks these candidates should 'share' ranks four and five and each be given a rank of 4.5.

Table 12.2 gives for these top candidates the rankings in each subject and the total of those ranks. The candidates are arranged in increasing order of total rank (given in the fifth column) – the lowest total corresponding, of course, to the best performance. For comparative purposes we give in the final column the rankings based on the total marks (i.e. the rankings given on p.159).

Table 12.2.   *Individual subject rankings for eight candidates*

Candidate	Maths rank	Eng. rank	Total rank	Rank based on total rank	Rank based on total mark
9	2	3.5	5.5	1	2
27	4	2	6	2	3
13	3	3.5	6.5	3.5	4
38	5.5	1	6.5	3.5	5
11	1	7	8	5	1
39	5.5	5.5	11	6	6
35	8	5.5	13.5	7	7
36	7	8	15	8	8

Have we not now perhaps been too harsh on candidate Number 11? He drops from first to fifth position. His very high mark in mathematics now confers no special advantage. Indeed, by replacing marks by rank we are retaining the examiner's ordering of candidates but ignoring the *amount* by which an examiner assesses the differences between candidates. In mathematics the gap of seven marks between the top candidate on ninety-six and the second candidate on eighty-nine has been reduced to a rank difference of one. Whereas in English the gap of one mark between first and second candidate remains a rank gap of one and the mark difference of seven between the first and seventh candidate is almost retained as a rank difference of six. In Mathematics the mark difference between first and seventh ranked candidate (rank difference six) is $96 - 78 = 18$. Use your stem and leaf displays prepared in Exercise 12.1 to verify these statements.

Standardized marks

Can we do something that retains, to a large extent, the relative differences between candidates as reflected in the examiners' marks, yet makes the marks in the two subjects more directly comparable? One feels that on the whole it would be fairer if candidates near the top in Mathematics and in English got much the same marks, as did the mid-range candidates and also the bottom candidates. We can achieve something like this making use of the mean and standard deviation of our data.

Exercise 12.4. Separately for the Mathematics and English marks in Table 12.1 calculate the mean and standard deviation.

Your tedious calculations should give:

> For Mathematics: Mean 50.7. Standard deviation 22.20
> For English: Mean 50.0. Standard deviation 15.77

The usual kind of standardization is to shift the mean (if it is not already there) to fifty, by adding or subtracting some appropriate value from each mark after 'scaling' them so that on the new scale the standard deviation will have some pre-specified value. We shall take this to be fifteen. Clearly we see that the examiner's marks in English already very nearly comply with both these conditions. Indeed our procedure will alter them only slightly. The Mathematics marks however have a much larger standard deviation (consistent with the greater spread, see p. 158).

If we rescale these to get a set of marks with standard deviation fifteen, the top marks will be reduced and the lower marks increased. Those near the mean will be changed only slightly.

There is of course an arbitrariness in standardizing in a way that affects the English marks very little but the Mathematics marks appreciably. However, had we worked the other way and scaled both sets of marks to have a standard deviation of about twenty-two we would have altered the English marks appreciably but had little effect on the Mathematics marks. Either way, a ranking based on the sum of standardized marks would be likely to show little difference. The reason scaling to a standard deviation of fifteen has some intuitive appeal is that if we had marks for a whole battery of subjects it is a common experience that for a wide range of subjects (Mathematics being the most usual exception) we often find examiners using a percentage scale will, for a large group of candidates, produce marks with a standard deviation close to fifteen. The mean tends to vary from subject to subject depending upon examination conventions, but fifty is a reasonable arbitrary choice. Psychologists often scale marks to a mean of fifty, but a standard deviation of ten rather than fifteen, calling the resulting mark a 'T-score'.

The procedure for producing marks standardized to mean fifty and standard deviation fifteen is straightforward. If the 'raw' examiner's marks have a mean m and standard deviation s, then if x is an examiner's mark we carry through the process in the flow diagram Figure 12.1 to obtain the standardized mark y.

This is equivalent to using a formula

$$y = \frac{15}{s}(x - m) + 50.$$

For the Mathematics marks $s = 22.2$ and $m = 50.7$. For candidate Number 1, $x = 54$ and following through the flow diagram and rounding the result to the nearest whole number we find $y = 52$.

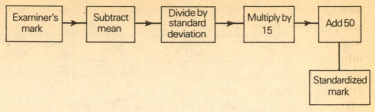

Figure 12.1. Flow diagram for standardizing marks.

If examiners can only award marks to an integral value it would be nonsensical to expect our standardized mark to have any meaningful higher degree of accuracy.

It is not hard to verify that for Mathematics candidates the formula above reduces to

$$y = 0.6757x + 15.74.$$

For English $m = 50.0$ and $s = 15.77$. We may standardize the English marks using these values in the flow diagram in Figure 12.1 or by using the formula

$$y = 0.9512x + 2.44.$$

Exercise 12.5. For the candidates numbered 1 to 5 in Table 12.1, calculate their standardized marks in both Mathematics and English. A pocket calculator helps.

We have calculated the standarized marks for all candidates and these and their totals are given in Table 12.3.

Exercise 12.6. Form stem and leaf displays and give five-number summaries for the standardized marks in each subject and compare the summaries using a box plot. Compare these five-number summaries with those for the marks in Table 12.1.

Exercise 12.7. Arrange in rank order the best eight candidates based on the total of the standardized marks given in Table 12.3.

Table 12.3.   *Standardized examination marks,*
            mean 50, s.d. 15

Candidate	Mathematics	English	Total
1	52	57	109
2	53	60	113
3	59	59	118
4	29	28	57
5	25	26	51
6	23	33	56
7	54	51	105
8	54	54	108
9	76	71	147
10	56	60	116
11	81	69	150
12	31	25	56
13	75	71	146
14	37	30	67
15	44	44	88
16	20	23	43
17	52	51	103
18	52	53	105
19	52	48	100
20	28	23	51
21	43	43	86
22	54	60	114
23	45	48	93
24	45	50	95
25	45	43	88
26	30	23	53
27	73	75	148
28	48	43	91
29	48	51	99
30	50	47	97
31	50	54	104
32	55	51	106
33	51	47	98
34	37	38	75
35	65	70	135
36	68	63	131
37	40	44	84
38	70	76	146
39	78	79	141
40	64	62	126

The rankings are given in the final column of Table 12.4, which also gives rank orders based on raw marks and on the rank totals for individual subjects given in the penultimate column of Table 12.2.

Ranking on standardized marks, candidate 11 retains the first place he got with the raw marks but he is now only two marks ahead of his nearest rival compared with five for the raw marks. (See Table

Table 12.4. *Ranking of top candidates by three methods*

Candidate	Raw marks	Rank totals	Stand. marks
11	1	5	1
9	2	1	3
27	3	2	2
13	4	3.5	4.5
38	5	3.5	4.5
39	6	6	6
35	7	7	7
36	8	8	8

12.1.) Candidates 9 and 27 are interchanged for second and third position, but with only one mark difference between them. This was also the mark difference with the examiners' marks for these candidates. The juxtaposition may not be unfair as it reflects more credit for the second top mark in English being close to the top mark in that subject, whereas in Mathematics the second top mark was seven below the best.

However, in practice it is hardly fair to separate the candidates whose totals differ by only one mark on both a standardized and a raw scale. Any examiner who considers his marking is entirely objective and sufficiently precise to make a difference of one mark really meaningful is probably deluding himself, but that is another matter, more properly belonging to considerations of *precision and accuracy*.

The method given above for standardizing marks may not be appropriate in all circumstances. For example, if a very specialized group enters for a subject it is likely that the performance of individuals will be good because they have chosen that specialist subject since it appeals to them or they are good at it. It might be quite unfair to reduce marks to a mean of fifty and standard deviation of fifteen if indeed such a group had all got marks, say, between forty-five and seventy. Very elaborate procedures are used by some universities to adjust marks of, for example, specialized honours degree candidates, before deciding the class of honours to be awarded.

Adjustment of examination marks by a scaling factor alone (i.e. multiplying each by a constant) is not uncommon, but the subject is a specialized one we shall not explore here.

13 Index numbers

Why are they needed?

'At one o'clock today the *Financial Times* index was up 0.8 at 972.5,' is a familiar type of item in a British radio newscast. In America it would be the Dow Jones, in Tokyo the Nikkei Dow, in Hong Kong the Hang Seng, in Sydney the AO and in Paris the CAC index. We often see references to other indices; the retail price index and the index of industrial production are two examples.

An index is a numerical yardstick to measure average changes with time, in essence a sophisticated summary statistic. The practical computation of any worthwhile index is often both complex and costly; their interpretation needs care and common sense rather than special skills.

A simple index

Example 13.1.   To illustrate the basic concepts and some of the problems of constructing an index we start with a simple example – an index to measure retail price changes for butter. We base our index on the price on 1 January 1983 and our aim is to measure prices at later dates *relative to* that price. The convention is to give our index the value 100 on the starting date, called the *base*. Suppose a 250 gm pack of butter costs 46p at our base date of 1 January 1983 and a similar pack costs 49p on 1 July 1983 and 48p on 1 January 1984. Our index is 100 on our *base date* when the price is 46p. To determine the index on 1 July 1983 we argue that since the price has risen three units from the base price of 46p to a new price of 49p, then the index value of 100 should rise in the same proportion, i.e. the new index value is given by

$$\text{new index} = 100 \times \frac{49}{46}$$

To one decimal place this has the value 106.5.

This implies that if we purchase on 1 July 1983 the amount of butter that cost 100p on 1 January 1983 it will cost 106.5p.

Exercise 13.1. Based on information given above, determine the butter price index value at 1 January 1984.

You should get 104.3. We could set these results out in a small table:

Date	Index
1 Jan 83	100.0
1 Jul 83	106.5
1 Jan 84	104.3

or as a simple graph (Figure 13.1).

In the real world the above explanation is too glib. In any supermarket you may well see a dozen different brands of butter on offer with prices for a 250 gm pack varying by some 5 to 6p between brands. In a small store a brand selling in the supermarket at 44p

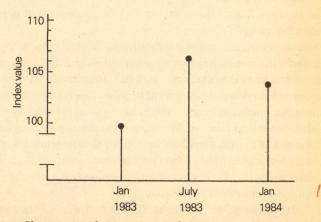

Figure 13.1. Changes in a butter price index.

may cost 47p. What then do we mean by saying that the price of butter on 1 January 1983 is 46p? Does it refer to one particular brand in one supermarket at that date? If this be so, for our index to have any meaning the prices quoted for later dates should refer to the same brand in the same supermarket. In this situation calling our index simply a *butter price index* could be misleading. What happens for one brand in one supermarket may be atypical of the general pattern of butter prices. The brand may be a high-priced one with small sales and the changes in price over a year may be smaller (or perhaps larger) than that for a range of more popular brands. It could be part of a loss-leader policy. There may be rather different changes for the same brand in other stores. Such a restricted index would be of little interest to anyone but the customers of that particular supermarket who regularly buy that brand of butter.

Possible improvements

A more interesting index would be one that reflected average price movements in butter for the whole country, or a substantial part of it. The average price paid per butter pack of 250 gm could be calculated exactly if we knew the total number of packs sold in, say, a given week, at each price. We could then calculate an average price in the form of a weighted mean (see p. 147). We would need this information for our base date and any others on which we wanted to calculate an index value.

Of course this is quite impracticable. It would be very costly to collect information from every retail outlet in Britain even with co-operation from shopkeepers – virtually impossible without that co-operation. In practice if we want to get some estimate of the average price paid for butter in retail stores throughout the country we would conduct a sample survey. We say a little about planning surveys in Chapters 14 and 15. It suffices here to say that if good survey practice is adopted information from a small proportion of retail outlets about prices and sales gives a close approximation to the average price per pack paid for butter on any given date.

If the prices given above for 1 January 1983, 1 July 1983 and 1 January 1984 were obtained from such a survey then we have a reasonable index for the average prices paid for butter at the various dates.

Interpretation of indices

Such an index is still open to misinterpretation. Suppose, for example, that a group of housewives living in Wester Ross, Scotland, another living in South Wales and a third in London all carry out separate surveys to determine the average retail price of butter *in their areas*; they are likely to come up with noticeably different average prices on, say, 1 July 1983. This results from price variations between different parts of the country, so an index based on national averages may not reflect what is happening in a particular area. It is therefore important in trying to understand an index to know its *field of applicability*. If a butter index is based on a 'national' average price important local variations (due to increased freight charges, establishment of a new supermarket in an area, etc.) will be ignored. Conversely, a local index calculated on the basis of price changes in that area may give a distorted picture of the national situation.

Comprehensive indices

An index such as the UK Retail Price Index takes into account price movements across a broad field of consumer expenditure. We give more detail of its construction on p. 172. As an intermediate step in explaining the construction of indices we consider next an index for two commodities.

Example 13.2. Suppose we wish to construct a national index for the price of pepper and butter.

To reflect changes in expenditure we must not only consider movements in the prices of unit packages of pepper and butter, but make allowance for the relative amounts of each bought by housewives. This will vary from household to household. Surveys may once again be used to get an *average* figure. Suppose a survey shows the average purchase of butter per head of population is 220 gm per week and that of pepper 0.5 gm per week. Let us again take the base date as 1 January 1983 and suppose the average retail prices then are 17p per 20 gm pack for pepper and 46p per 250 gm pack for butter. To be realistic we form a *price* index that takes account of quantities purchased. That is, we work out the average weekly *expenditure* per person on pepper and butter. Now since the average person purchases (or has purchased on their behalf) 0.5 gm of pepper at a price of 17p per 20 gm this costs $(0.5/20) \times 17 = 17/40 = 0.425$p. Similarly the expenditure on 220 gm of butter at 46p per 250 gm is $(220/250) \times 46 = 40.48$p. The combined weekly expenditure is thus $40.48 + 0.425 = 40.905$p.

It is immediately evident that since expenditure on pepper is negligible compared to that on butter, a quite sharp change in the price of pepper will have less effect on total pepper plus butter expenditure than a similar percentage change in the price of butter.

To calculate the index for 1 July 1983 if pepper prices double to 34p per 20 gm while butter prices only rise to 49 pence per 250 gm we shall assume the consumption rates remain the same. Then the weekly cost per person for these two items becomes $(0.5/20) \times 34 + (220/250) \times 49 = 43.97$p. (Check carefully you understand why by comparing with the way we worked out the 1 January expenditure on these items.)

To calculate the butter and pepper index for 1 July with base 100 at 1 January, we simply multiply the price ratio $43.97/40.905$ by 100, giving 107.49.

In the above example since the price of pepper doubled, a pepper alone index would have risen from 100 to 200; the price of butter rose only from 46 to 49, representing a rise in a butter alone index (see p. 167) from 100 to 106.5. What we have done in calculating the combined index is to 'weight' prices per (arbitrary) unit – 250 gm for butter and 20 gm for pepper – by the number of units consumed, i.e. 0.5/20 for pepper, and 220/250 for butter. Convenient pricing units generally vary, as here, from commodity to commodity. In the UK meat is usually priced per pound, milk per pint, eggs per dozen, and so on. On the Continent, or in Australia, meat is priced per kilogram and milk per litre (or sometimes per 600 ml carton).

Exercise 13.2.   To illustrate a point made above that a specific percentage change in the price of a commodity with a higher weighting (e.g. weekly expenditure) has a more dramatic effect on the index, suppose the price of butter doubled while that of pepper rose only slightly, i.e. butter increased from 46 to 92p per 250 gm but pepper only from 17 to 20p per 20 gm. What then is the change in our pepper and butter index taken with base 100 on 1 January 1983?

Your calculations (see p. 283) should give you a value of 199.1. Doubling the price of butter (the heavy item of expenditure) has a much greater effect than doubling the price of pepper (a relatively small expenditure item).

If we have two commodities and we denote the price of the first at the base date for the index by $p_1(o)$ and the price at the current date at which we want to calculate the index by $p_1(c)$ and corresponding prices for a second commodity by $p_2(o)$ and $p_2(c)$, (the 'c' standing for current), then if q_1 and q_2 are the quantities (numbers of units) of each purchased by each individual the price index at the current time, c, is

$$I = \frac{q_1 p_1(c) + q_2 p_2(c)}{q_1 p_1(o) + q_2 p_2(o)} \times 100$$

This idea may be extended to three or more commodities, an additional product term being added in both numerator and denominator for each extra commodity. In the numerator (top line) the product is the quantity (number of units purchased) multiplied by the current price per unit and in the denominator (bottom line) it is the quantity multiplied by the base-date price per unit. We may look upon the index as the quotient of two weighted means (or more precisely two weighted totals) of prices, the result being multiplied by 100. The weights are the per capita consumption.

A further complication

If the price of butter doubles it is likely that many people will buy less butter; the average quantity consumed might fall from 220 to 190 gm per week. This suggests adjustments we should make in calculating the index. For butter (commodity number two in the formula given above) we took $q_2 = 220/250$. Would it be more appropriate to replace this by 190/250? It would certainly seem appropriate to do this in the numerator, but before making a decision pause and think what our index is supposed to measure. If, in a formula like that for calculating *I* given above, we want to compare what *price* we would have to pay now for the amounts consumed at the *base* date it is appropriate to use q_1 and q_2 representative of the base date. If we want to compare prices for our current consumption with what we would have paid for those amounts at the base date we should use q_1 and q_2 to represent our *current* consumption. If we use base date *quantity* weights for our index the index is often referred to as a *Laspeyres* price index. If we use current *quantity* weights it is called a *Paasche* price index.

It seems tempting to use current quantities in the numerator and base date quantities in the denominator. This gives a meaningful index but it is *not* a price or cost index. It is rather an index of total expenditure on these commodities – it compares the average total expenditure on the commodities at the different times and takes account of changes both in price and in consumption.

A real index

We are now in a position to consider in broad terms how a real index is calculated. We look in some detail at the United Kingdom Index of Retail Prices (RPI) as it illustrates many of the strengths and weaknesses of the concept of an index.

Example 13.3. The RPI is calculated monthly and the weights used are revised annually on the basis of changing household expenditure patterns revealed by a nationwide survey called the *Family Expenditure Survey* carried out by the Central Statistical Office. The weights are applied to estimates of expenditure by an 'average' household on items under each of eleven headings. In any given year the weights for each group are based on information gleaned from the Family Expenditure Survey for the year ending in the previous June. We describe the Family Expenditure Survey in more detail in Chapter 15, p. 201. Table 13.1 gives the weights used for each of the eleven headings in 1962, 1973 and 1984. A decrease in

Table 13.1. *Weights (total 1000) used in RPI calculations*

	Food	Alcohol	Tobacco	Housing	Fuel and light	Durable household goods	Clothing and footwear	Transport and vehicles	Miscellaneous goods	Services	Meals outside home
1962	350	71	80	87	55	66	106	68	59	58	–
1973	248	73	49	126	58	58	89	135	65	53	46
1984	201	75	36	149	65	69	70	158	76	65	36

weight between any two dates indicates that families are on average spending a lower proportion of their income on items under that heading. The headings are Food, Alcohol, Tobacco, Housing, Fuel and light, Durable household goods, Clothing and footwear, Transport and vehicles, Miscellaneous Goods, Services, Meals outside home. This final category was not included in the index in 1962.

The weights for any given heading change with time. The table implies that in 1962 the average family spent over 10 per cent of their income (106 parts per 1000) on clothing, but by 1984 only 7 per cent (70 parts per 1000) on clothing, whereas the proportion spent on transport and vehicles increased from just over one-fifteenth to nearly one-sixth. Note that even had there been no changes in proportional expenditure the introduction of the additional category *meals outside home* would alter the weights in other categories if the total is maintained at 1000. One would expect the biggest basic effect of introducing this category to be on the weightings for food and perhaps alcohol.

Exercise 13.3.   In Table 13.1, which of the eleven categories shows the largest relative change in weighting between 1962 and 1984? Which category shows the largest relative increase in weighting between 1973 and 1984?

The prices used in calculating the index cover items under the various heads of expenditure listed in Table 13.1. This leaves some noteworthy exclusions. The chief factors not taken into account are: (i) income tax payments; (ii) national insurance contributions; (iii) pension and life insurance premiums; (iv) subscriptions to trade unions and professional bodies; and (v) the capital element of mortgage repayments.

Other exclusions are contributions to church collections, cash gifts, betting, doctors' and dentists' fees. Although the capital element of mortgage repayments is excluded, interest repayments on mortgages are included, as are rent payments.

With a base of 100 at 1 January 1974, the index stood at 189.5 on 1 January 1978 and at 358.5 on 1 December 1984.

The idea of revising the weights annually is a slight compromise *vis-à-vis* the use of exact current weights. The Family Expenditure Survey is an annual event and provides a sensible basis for re-evaluation of weights. It would be a needlessly costly business to carry out this survey each month as patterns do not usually change suddenly or dramatically except in crisis situations like the outbreak of war or the introduction of rationing.

The other important information needed to calculate the index is a set of average prices for many commodities. For expenditure within each category a representative list of items is selected and priced at regular intervals from a wide selection of urban and retail outlets throughout the United Kingdom. So far as is possible goods of unchanged quality are priced at successive dates – clearly an aim that will sometimes be difficult to achieve, particularly in areas like vehicles and durable goods where new models are constantly being introduced and older ones withdrawn.

Use and abuse

Much criticism of the RPI arises from misconceptions about how it is constructed and about what it is supposed to measure. An essential point to note is that it is based on *average* prices nationwide and the items included are commodities or services used by the great majority of households in the UK, including practically all wage-earners and most small and medium salary earners. Obviously the expenditure pattern of a single person living alone is likely to be very different from that of a married couple with five young children – again, a single person's on a low income is probably very different from that of one on a high income.

Changes in the RPI are often regarded as a measure of inflation and one hears people say, 'Inflation is only supposed to have gone up 5 per cent last year, but my expenses have gone up 10 per cent.' It could well be true. But has the person based his statement on expenditure or prices covered by the RPI? Are the weightings used in the RPI relevant to that individual's expenditure, or does he, for example, spend appreciably less on drink than is implied by the alcohol weighting and more on clothes than the weighting for them implies? The author spends considerably more on alcohol than on clothing, yet both get very similar weights in 1984 (Table 13.1) for RPI calculations. Also, price changes in a local area may not be reflected in the national average.

The tax and prices index

To a taxpayer the omission of income tax from RPI calculations may seem surprising. The level of personal taxation has a marked effect on our disposable income, but, unlike indirect taxes such as value-added tax, it has little effect on prices. A rather different index exists to take into account the effect of direct taxes as well as prices on the cost of living. It is called the *Taxes and price index* or TPI for short.

The aim of the TPI is to measure the increase in gross taxable income needed to compensate taxpayers for any increase in retail prices, i.e. how much more a person must earn gross to keep up with the RPI. Thus a TPI of 110 implies I need a 10 per cent increase in gross income to have the same spending power *after tax* as I had when the TPI was 100.

A newer concept than the RPI, it is a useful index, but sadly it has become a political football. When it has been rising more slowly than the RPI a Government intent upon dampening wage demands has readily extolled its virtues as a basis for wage negotiations where 'cost of living' is an important part of the argument for an increase. When it rises more rapidly than the RPI it loses much of its glamour in ministerial eyes.

As well as changes in retail prices, the TPI takes into account changes in income-tax liability and also changes in *employees'* national insurance contributions. For this reason non-taxpayers are excluded from the calculations as their situation is effectively covered by the RPI. Those with incomes over £17 000 per annum as at 1 January 1984 are also excluded since changes in their tax liabilities are not necessarily representative of the majority of taxpayers. People in this class represent about 4 per cent of all tax-payers. The exclusion is not unreasonable since special tax scales apply to higher incomes. Broadly the same group are excluded from RPI calculations.

A few items such as non-taxable child benefits are excluded from the TPI. The TPI is constructed so as to reflect changes in tax liabilities. It does not reflect *actual* payments for this would make it subject to highly erratic movements which would be hard to interpret.

The distribution of gross taxable income is estimated from the *Inland Revenue Survey of Personal Incomes*. This is discussed briefly in Chapter 15, p. 202. Because of delays in processing survey data the TPI in, for example, 1984 was based on the 1981–82 survey.

Between budgets the TPI normally rises slightly faster than the RPI because a greater than proportional increase in gross income is needed to offset price rises since, under the UK tax system, all *extra* income is fully taxed once income passes the exemption and low rate thresholds.

Any changes in direct taxation, specifically those associated with the Chancellor's annual Budget may have a marked effect on the TPI.

Changing the base year

Currently the base date for the retail price index when its value was 100 is January 1974. The TPI had value 100 in January 1978 so the December 1984 values of 358.5 and 183.9 are in no way comparable.

There is nothing sacrosanct about a particular base year for an index – the only important thing is that we can only make direct comparisons of two indices (should such comparisons be relevant) if they have the same base year. At 1 January 1978 the RPI had the value 189.5. We may convert our current RPI of 358.5 relative to the 1974 base to a 1978 base of 100 using the following argument: since 189.5 increases to 358.5 then the proportionate increase from 100 would be (358.5/189.5) × 100 = 189.18. This figure of 189.18 for a 1978 base of 100 is very similar to the TPI value of 183.9. The lower value of the TPI is probably a reflection of a shift from direct to indirect taxation; while any indirect tax increases will be reflected in the RPI, a number of other factors such as costs of raw materials, manufacturing costs, etc., also get more weight in RPI calculations than in TPI calculations.

We may wish to change the base year of an index not only for comparison with related indices but because an index attains a value so far removed from its notional base of 100 that changes become difficult to interpret. During periods of rapid inflation any index of prices will climb steeply. Had we taken the year 1900 as the base year for the RPI it would probably now have a value of many thousands.

Choice of base year (and some particular index) is a favourite political game. Popular claims such as 'we are spending more on education *in real terms* than ever before' seldom stand up to too close a scrutiny; they often depend for their truth very critically on the choice of a base year and an appropriate measure of inflation. The inflation rate for educational expenditure may not be that implied by the broadly based RPI. The pattern of school expenditure on equipment, teachers' salaries, etc., is different from the pattern of household spending.

The old chestnut attributed to Disraeli that there are lies, damned lies and statistics could appropriately be rephrased *there are liars, damned liars and politicians.*

Incidentally, there is no magic in selecting 100 as a base. This is purely conventional. The recently introduced London Stock Exchange 100 share index has a base of 1000. One suspects 1000 was chosen to make it broadly comparable to the much older *Financial Times* Ordinary Share Index (commonly called the FT index, though it is only one of several indices published by the *Financial Times*) which then had a value hovering around 900. The *Financial Times* Ordinary Share Index, incidentally, is based on share price changes for a limited group of 30 companies, whereas the London Stock Exchange 100 share index is based on a more representative group of 100 companies. The base date for the current (June 1985) FT index is 1 July 1935.

Price indices and purchasing power

If we regard the RPI as a measure of purchasing power of money then an increase from 100 to 200 means that the purchasing power of money is halved. Goods or services purchasable for £1.00 in the base year now cost £2.00. Looked at another way, goods which cost £1.00 in the current year could have been purchased for 50 pence in the base year.

Given the retail price index for each year we can easily draw up a table of changes in the purchasing power of the pound. We have seen that the RPI was 189.5 in January 1978 and 358.5 in December 1984. Denoting the purchasing power of £1.00 as 100 in January 1978, then in December 1984 the amount needed for an equivalent purchase would be 100 × (358.5/189.5) = 189p (to the nearest penny). Similarly the goods which in December 1984 cost £1.00 could be purchased in January 1978 for 100 × (189.5/358.5) = 53p.

Table 13.2 shows how the purchasing power of the pound as measured by the RPI has changed over each four-year period between 1968 and 1984. Along the diagonal running down from left to right the entries are all 100. If we read down any column we see how the purchasing power of a pound taken as 100p in the year given at the head of that column has changed with time. For example, if we look at the column headed 1972 we see that in 1968 we could have bought for £1.00 goods costing 131p in 1972, whereas in 1984 our pound will only purchase goods that we could have got for 24p in 1972. Reading across the row labelled 1976 we see that goods costing £1.00 in 1976 would cost £2.24 in 1984, whereas they could have been purchased for 42p in 1968.

Table 13.2.   *The changing pound*

	1968	1972	1976	1980	1984
1968	100	131	241	404	539
1972	76	100	183	308	410
1976	42	55	100	168	224
1980	25	32	60	100	133
1984	19	24	45	75	100

Exercise 13.4. How much would I have to pay in 1980 for goods costing £1.00 in 1968? How much would I have had to pay in 1972 for goods that cost £1.00 in 1980? What would I have to pay in 1984 for goods that cost £1.00 in 1968?

Further reading

Index numbers are discussed in some detail by Yeomans (1968, Chapter 4) and by Moore (1980, Chapter 5), as well as in most elementary books on business statistics.

4 Some Statistical Ideas

14 Sample surveys – some basics

What data should we collect?

The computer breakdown data in Chapter 1 stemmed from routine collection of information. So did our rainfall records, observations on traffic flow, and so on.

In Chapter 13 we studied several indices, in particular the UK Retail Price Index, referring to necessary but costly and elaborate methods of collecting key information on expenditure patterns and prices, the former from an official exercise called the *Family Expenditure Survey*. Surveys are important when we need information that is not already available from existing or routine records. In essence a *survey* – more formally a *sample survey* – refers to a situation where information is collected only for some of the units in which one is interested. To get useful results, the information obtained must be relevant and the units chosen so that they will give a reasonable reflection of what the situation would be if information had been gathered for all units in which we are interested.

Population and sample

Two important pieces of statistical jargon are used in this context. The total set of units of interest is called the *population*. This may or may not be a population in the everyday sense of the word; it could be all citizens of the UK, or the EEC, or the United States, or Australia. A biologist studying the breeding habits of insects may be interested in one particular species in one region in the United Kingdom. All insects of that species in that region would be the population in which he was interested.

The population need not be one of people or animals. An inspector of motor vehicles may be interested in characteristics of all motor cars in Wales with an engine rating less than 1600 cc. His population is all such cars in Wales.

The population units need not always be individuals or single items, but may be some grouping of these. Indeed, the *Family Expenditure Survey*, as its name implies, deals with units which are families or households. The exact sense in which we here use the term family will be defined on p. 201. In many situations our population may be hypothetical in that it covers, for example, all cars under 1600 cc capacity that have been or will be made in a certain factory, or all pigs of a certain breed that exist now or did in the past or will in the future.

The second piece of jargon is the word *sample*. A sample is a subset of the units of a population. In a *sample survey* we measure characteristics of interest on selected units only (the *sample*) and use our results to make inferences about a *population*. It differs from a census where data is collected for the whole population.

Example 14.1.   A sample survey is useful only if the information it gives *broadly* mirrors that relevant to the whole population. For example, suppose we observe 100 adult Londoners and find that ninety-four of them smoke cigarettes. Can we conclude that approximately 94 per cent of all adult Londoners smoke cigarettes?

This question is unanswerable unless we know something about how the sample was obtained. If the sample happened to be 100 people who were attending a meeting to protest about a proposed doubling of the tax on cigarettes it is likely that those attending would not be a typical cross-section of Londoners; they would more likely be people with a vested interest in the tax proposal – people who were going to have to foot the bill because they were heavy smokers, plus some associated with the tobacco trade who saw in the tax proposals a threat to their industry or jobs. Intuitively one would expect the proportion of smokers in such a 'sample' to be greater than that for Londoners as a whole. Non-smokers other than any among the tobacco industry representatives would be unlikely to attend.

To avoid dangers of making erroneous generalizations about population characteristics based on sample observations where the sample is unrepresentative, our selection of the sample must be soundly based and not just a matter of convenience.

Wrong questions – wrong sample

Example 14.2. In case it be thought the example just given is un-realistic let us return to the survey mentioned in Chapter 1, p. 22, on 'VDU operators and health hazards', originating in the journal *Health and Safety at Work*, often referred to as *HS*. Not only was this questionnaire not sent to a recognizable sample of any specific population of VDU users, but it failed to ask questions in a way that would give sound information on health hazards attributable to VDU operation.

Distribution of the questionnaire was entrusted, in part at any rate, to certain trade unions with members who worked on VDUs. The assistant secretary of one of these unions wrote a letter to the editor of *HS* highly critical of the questionnaire but saying she had never-theless circulated it to some 1000 of their safety representatives. The health and safety officer of another leading trade union wrote to *HS* in equally critical terms adding that she could not recommend their members to take part. The medical officer of one of the largest UK industrial firms and the safety officer of a brewery both wrote con-demning the survey. To their credit *HS* published these com-plaints.

As the sample who responded was essentially self-selecting among those who happened to receive the questionnaire from one of a variety of sources, there is a high likelihood that it would consist largely of people in two categories, i.e. (i) those who had health problems that could be, or they believed could be, attri-buted to working with VDUs or (ii) those who had a vested interest in demonstrating that VDUs presented, or did not present, a health hazard. *HS* reported receipt of some 1200 replies within a month of publication of the questionnaire.

Among faults pointed out in correspondence were (i) the self-selecting property referred to above, (ii) the absence of any controls (non-VDU workers) to assess the prevalence of disorders ranging from eyestrain to backache and loss of feeling in fingers or wrists mentioned in the questionnaire, (iii) the failure to ask for detailed information on the type of VDU and (iv) the omission of any request for information about how long the respondent had been working on a VDU. The journal invited replies saying 'the questionnaires will be analysed and a full report published'. Any such analysis is likely to be worthless.

Had the advice of a medical statistician been sought in designing the questionnaire and selecting a suitable sample (of VDU workers and other office workers) useful information might have been obtained as to whether the introduction of this modern technological device into the office was having an adverse effect on health, and further whether any problems were specific to particular types of VDU. The editor's published defence of the exercise that 'I was fully aware of the limitations of the kind of questionnaire that can be issued through a magazine like *HS*' is hardly an excuse for a time-wasting exercise that can only bring unease about, even ridicule upon, survey methods. All this is rather sad as one would like hard evidence to know if VDUs are in any way – as is thought by some – a health hazard. If it were established that they are, then there would be strong incentives for, even a moral obligation on, governments, manufacturers and users to seek a remedy.

Basic types of samples

Basically, there are two satisfactory ways of obtaining samples that can reasonably be expected to mirror information on a population. We must seek either a *representative sample* or use what is called a *random sample*. Both these broad concepts give rise to a number of variants and refinements.

One of the best-known uses of samples to obtain information relevant to a population is in opinion polls, used widely in market research as well as to canvass people's views on political and social matters. Nearly all polls of this type are based on a refinement of *representative sampling* called *quota sampling*.

Example 14.3. In essence a quota sample aims to get a sample balanced with respect to several characteristics which it is known will, or it is suspected may, influence responses to the survey. To take the example of the proportion of smokers among Londoners it is likely that age, sex, income, educational status, social class, ethnic origin and religious beliefs might influence one's decision about smoking. A quota sample would aim to have these various 'factors', so far as is possible, balanced so that the sample proportions approximate to those in the population, e.g. about half the sample would be men, half would be women, people of various ages would be included roughly in the same proportions as among Londoners as a whole. It seems unlikely that the colour of people's eyes or whether they preferred cats to dogs as pets would influence smoking habits, so these factors would not be taken into account in selecting a quota sample to assess smoking habits.

Quota samples

To obtain a sample each interviewer is given a *quota* of respondents to interview. Different poll organizations have different approaches to selecting quotas, but to illustrate the principles, one interviewer may be told to interview ten people, five male and five female, two of each sex to be under forty and three over forty; of the two males under forty one should be a manual worker, the other professional; of the three over forty, one should be a manual worker, one unemployed but below pensionable age and one over pension age. For the younger females the specification may be that one is working, the other a housewife, and for the three over forty he might be told to interview one in employment, one housewife under pensionable age and one widowed pensioner. In addition he might be told that of the ten he interviews exactly two should be non-white. The interviewer may be given further instructions, e.g. that half the interviews should take place in the street during daylight hours and half by calls to residential houses in the evening and that not more than two should be conducted in any one street and that half should be in areas north of the Thames and half south of the Thames.

Apart from such broad instructions the interviewer is free to choose which individuals shall constitute his sample of ten. Here one of the weaknesses of 'quota' sampling shows up. There is a danger that the interviewer will show some subjectivity in selecting a sample. For example, for the five people he has to contact in the street he may well wish to avoid approaching people who look as though they may be aggressive. He may feel people who obviously look to be in a hurry will resent being interviewed and thus only approach people who look friendly and do not seem to be pressed for time. Is there not a possibility that such people are less subjected to stresses and strains which, according to our views on these matters, may encourage one to smoke, or alternatively be a result of smoking too heavily?

Now our interviewer, being perhaps only one of a dozen who have each been asked to interview 10 people (giving a total sample of 120) may not have his inclination to interview only 'amenable' people shared by his fellow interviewers, so any biases of this sort may be balanced out by some other interviewer seeking out aggressive respondents – perhaps because he finds interviewing them more challenging! But there is no guarantee this will happen.

Thus we see that interviewers, while selecting their quota correctly, may unwittingly bias results because they allow another factor to limit their choice of respondents, e.g. reluctance to interview people who look difficult, or perhaps failing to visit areas where they feel people might become abusive or resent being interviewed. A well-trained interviewer is aware of such possible sources of bias and tries to avoid them, but there may be 'hidden' biases that are unthought of.

Another problem with quota sampling is that the sample can only be balanced with respect to a limited number of characteristics – age, sex, religion, social status, ethnic origin, for example – which it is felt might affect smoking habits, and we have no easy way of verifying whether our choice is correct. A factor may be overlooked because it is not obvious, or ignored because it is difficult to classify people on some criterion. For example, aggressiveness may be allied to smoking habits, but how many people in a community might be classified as very aggressive, moderately aggressive or docile? How might an interviewer 'select' individuals on the basis of such criteria? His intentions might be misconstrued if he approached a lady in the street with, 'Excuse me, madam, but are you docile?' Finally, can we be sure smoking habits are not influenced by some completely unexpected factor — such as the sign of the zodiac for one's birthday!

The net result of all these difficulties is that there is no objective way of deciding how 'accurate' a reflection of the population situation is given by a quota sample. The method is widely used in opinion polls and market research. When the results can be checked — as for example in opinion polls held just before an election or referendum — these polls, if well conducted, are generally found to be accurate to within 2 or 3 per cent when predicting proportions in the 30–70 per cent range, i.e. if a British opinion poll carried out by an experienced polling organization predicts immediately before an election a Tory vote of 47 per cent the actual vote is very likely to be in the range 45–49 per cent, but there is always a *sampling* error that means a possible deviation of this order from the population value.

There have been some spectacular failures of poll predictions. These might be attributable to a breakdown in the quota sampling method — e.g. some factor may be influencing voting intentions that has not been taken into account in selecting the quota, or it might reflect last-minute changes of opinion on the part of the electorate; such changes may be due to a political leader making a blunder only hours before voting takes place, or the publication of disastrous trade figures on the eve of an election, but after the opinion poll has been conducted. By the nature of the UK electoral system a very small change in proportions voting for each party can have a dramatic effect on the numbers of seats won. Sometimes this change in proportions lies within the sampling error of some 2 per cent either way.

Despite their disadvantages, experienced pollsters have got the use of quota samples down to a fine art. A carefully selected quota sample of roughly fifteen hundred voters gives a good indication of the proportionate party vote for the whole United Kingdom at a parliamentary election; this despite the fact that there are vast differences in voting patterns throughout the UK from the so-called Tory strongholds of south-east England to the Labour bastions of northeast England and Scotland.

The great advantage of quota sampling is that it is relatively cheap; its main disadvantage, even when skilfully conducted, is that there is no theoretical (or practical) way of deciding how accurately it mirrors population patterns unless it is followed up by a *census* (which is virtually what a parliamentary election is with regard to voting patterns). The pragmatic approach is that in skilled hands it works reasonably well.

Random samples

Random samples provide a mechanism whereby we can make an estimate of a population characteristic and get, based on probability theory, a numerical measure of how good that estimate is. The detail of how to get these measures of precision is beyond the scope of this book, but an indication of the techniques and problems of random sampling is given in this and the next chapter – not as a definitive account of the method, but to give some idea of the scope and importance of this method of data collection. If you have a data-collection problem where the approach seems appropriate the best advice we can give is to consult a trained statistician before using the method.

Suppose there are N units in the population; then a random sample of n units (where n is a number less than N) is one of all the possible samples of that size *selected at random*; a phrase meaning that every one of those samples has an equal chance of being the one chosen. In practice if we have a population of size N we may select a random sample of size n (where n is any number less than N) by a process that selects the first member of the sample in a way that gives every unit in the population an equal chance (*probability* is the more formal technical term) of selection. The second sample member is selected in a similar way from the remaining $N - 1$ members of the population by a process giving each an equal chance of selection; the procedure continuing for the third, fourth and fifth member and so on until all *n* sample units are selected.

While the theory is simple, the practice of random sampling is not. To select a random sample we need in essence a complete listing of all units in a population and a mechanism whereby we can select units with an equal chance of choosing any unit. The list of all units in a population is called a *sampling frame*. Given a frame, the ideal mechanism for selecting samples is a set of *random numbers*. Providing a set of random numbers (or something for all purposes equivalent and more properly called *pseudo-random numbers*) is a routine activity for any computer, using a built-in mathematical black box that is a standard part of modern computer software. We must however issue one note of caution about these black boxes – some do the job less well than others, as we find in Chapter 17, Example 17.3, p. 220.

Sampling frames

Sometimes we are lucky and an adequate (even if not perfect) sampling frame is quickly available. If we are interested in a random sample of all adults in the electorate of Hillhead (a Glasgow suburban area) or any other UK parliamentary constituency, the electoral register provides such a list. It will not be 100 per cent accurate since it is only revised annually. In particular, the list will contain a few people who have died since the last revision and will exclude some who would have been entitled to vote apart from their names having been accidentally omitted from the register. Some newcomers to the district will be omitted and the names of some people who have moved from the district will be included. By and large the list is an accurate record of adults living in the area (residency being the prime criterion for a voting right).

Again, if we wished to use survey methods to estimate the number of misprints per page in the manuscript of a book we might do this by taking a random sample of pages. Suppose the book has 620 pages, the 620 numbered pages represent a frame. We could use 50 randomly chosen numbers between 1 and 620 to select a sample of 50 pages and count the number of misprints on each.

You may ask, why go to this trouble. Would it not suffice just to count the number of misprints on each of the first 50 pages? A moment's reflection will show that to do so might lead to bias, particularly if the book were of a technical nature, because many such books become more complex in their subject matter as they proceed and the danger of misprints in writing, typing and setting up and checking more complex typography becomes greater.

If we wanted to determine the total area under wheat in the Republic of Ireland, choice of a sampling frame is less obvious. It could be based on a map and random selection of grid references. An account of sample selection methods based on maps is given by Yates (1981, Chapter 4).

Selecting random samples

Suppose that we have a sampling frame that enables us to identify each member of the population uniquely by a number. For a population with N units there is no loss of generality in choosing these numbers to be the ordered integers $1, 2, 3, \ldots N$.

To select a random sample of size n, what in theory we do is first select a random number between 1 and N. A computer will do this for us using what is called a random number generator (more properly a *pseudo*-random number generator). By giving a command like

RANDOM(N) or RND(N)

(your computer manual should tell you the precise form for your installation), the computer will produce a number which is equally likely to be any integer between 1 and N inclusive. By repeating this process it eventually produces a random sample of size n. If, in the process, a number already selected is repeated this must be rejected from the sample and a further random number chosen. In practice there are sophisticated ways of avoiding rejections if there are many repetitions, something that may happen with large samples. When n different random numbers have been chosen, the units in the population allocated these numbers form the random sample.

We consider uses and properties of such samples at a more technical level in the next chapter.

15 *Sample surveys*
– the nuts and bolts

Exploring random samples

To get the feel of what happens when we take random samples we shall look at a simple example. From a population of size $N = 9$ we will take samples of size $n = 4$. How many different samples can we get? Mathematicians have a formula for this, and it turns out to be 126. If you are surprised there are so many we set them all out for a particular case.

Example 15.1. Suppose we have nine pages of manuscript $(N = 9)$ prepared by a cub journalist and we are interested in the average number of alterations a sub-editor makes per page submitted by this journalist. Of course in this trivial example if we are given the data of Table 15.1 then it is very easy to see that the mean number of alterations is five. (Adding the bottom row we find a total of forty-five.) We now consider estimating this mean using a random sample of $n = 4$ pages.

Table 15.1. *Numbers of editorial corrections per page*

Page no.	1	2	3	4	5	6	7	8	9
No. corrections	0	3	1	9	4	7	11	8	2

We pointed out above that there are 126 different samples of four items from nine. If our sample turns out to be pages 2, 4, 5 and 8 the numbers of alterations on these pages are three, nine, four and eight respectively and the average number of alterations per page *in this sample* is obtained by dividing the total number $3 + 9 + 4 + 8 = 24$ by the number of pages in the sample, four, giving the average six (compared to the population average five).

Table 15.2 lists the numbers of corrections there are for all possible samples of four pages. For example, the first entry of 0, 3, 1, 9 corresponds to pages 1, 2, 3, 4; the second entry (reading across) of 0, 3, 1, 4 corresponds to pages 1, 2, 3, 5, and the tenth entry of 0, 3, 9, 8 corresponds to pages 1, 2, 4, 8.

Exercise 15.1.   A bit of a hard slog this – but not too bad with a pocket calculator. Compute the means of each sample of four in Table 15.2. You will find that some samples have identical means, but there is quite a range of mean values. Prepare a frequency table of these means *then* check if your table agrees with Table 15.3.

Table 15.2.   *Numbers of alterations for all samples of four pages*

0	3	1	9	0	3	1	4	0	3	1	7	0	3	1	11
0	3	1	8	0	3	1	2	0	3	9	4	0	3	9	7
0	3	9	11	0	3	9	8	0	3	9	2	0	3	4	7
0	3	4	11	0	3	4	8	0	3	4	2	0	3	7	11
0	3	7	8	0	3	7	2	0	3	11	8	0	3	11	2
0	3	8	2	0	1	9	4	0	1	9	7	0	1	9	11
0	1	9	8	0	1	9	2	0	1	4	7	0	1	4	11
0	1	4	8	0	1	4	2	0	1	7	11	0	1	7	8
0	1	7	2	0	1	11	8	0	1	11	2	0	1	8	2
0	9	4	7	0	9	4	11	0	9	4	8	0	9	4	2
0	9	7	11	0	9	7	8	0	9	7	2	0	9	11	8
0	9	11	2	0	9	8	2	0	4	7	11	0	4	7	8
0	4	7	2	0	4	11	8	0	4	11	2	0	4	8	2
0	7	11	8	0	7	11	2	0	7	8	2	0	11	8	2
3	1	9	4	3	1	9	7	3	1	9	11	3	1	9	8
3	1	9	2	3	1	4	7	3	1	4	11	3	1	4	8
3	1	4	2	3	1	7	11	3	1	7	8	3	1	7	2
3	1	11	8	3	1	11	2	3	1	8	2	3	9	4	7
3	9	4	11	3	9	4	8	3	9	4	2	3	9	7	11
3	9	7	8	3	9	7	2	3	9	11	8	3	9	11	2
3	9	8	2	3	4	7	11	3	4	7	8	3	4	7	2
3	4	11	8	3	4	11	2	3	4	8	2	3	7	11	8
3	7	11	2	3	7	8	2	3	11	8	2	1	9	4	7
1	9	4	11	1	9	4	8	1	9	4	2	1	9	7	11
1	9	7	8	1	9	7	2	1	9	11	8	1	9	11	2
1	9	8	2	1	4	7	11	1	4	7	8	1	4	7	2
1	4	11	8	1	4	11	2	1	4	8	2	1	7	11	8
1	7	11	2	1	7	8	2	1	11	8	2	9	4	7	11
9	4	7	8	9	4	7	2	9	4	11	8	9	4	11	2
9	4	8	2	9	7	11	8	9	7	11	2	9	7	8	2
9	11	8	2	4	7	11	8	4	7	11	2	4	7	8	2
4	11	8	2	7	11	8	2								

In the final column of Table 15.3 we give each frequency as a percentage (to one decimal place) of the total sample number, 126, e.g. nine out of 126 is $100 \times (9/126) = 7.1$.

In Table 15.3 why does the total percentage exceed 100?

A glance at the table shows that if we take a random sample of four from nine the sample mean may take a value between 1.5 and 8.75; neither of these extreme values are good estimates of the population mean of five! However, further inspection shows that sixty-nine samples out of 126 — slightly more than half — would give a

Table 15.3.   *Frequency table of means for 126 samples of four from nine items*

Mean	Frequency	Per cent of total
1.5	1	0.8
1.75	1	0.8
2	1	0.8
2.25	1	0.8
2.5	2	1.6
2.75	2	1.6
3	4	3.2
3.25	5	4.0
3.5	7	5.6
3.75	6	4.8
4	7	5.6
4.25	6	4.8
4.5	7	5.6
4.75	7	5.6
5	9	7.1
5.25	9	7.1
5.5	9	7.1
5.75	8	6.3
6	7	5.6
6.25	5	4.0
6.5	4	3.2
6.75	4	3.2
7	4	3.2
7.25	3	2.4
7.5	3	2.4
7.75	2	1.6
8	1	0.8
8.25	0	0.0
8.5	0	0.0
8.75	1	0.8
Total	126	100.4

mean between four and six; not too bad an estimate, you may feel, of a population mean with true value five when the nine observations range from zero to eleven.

Exercise 15.2.   Use Table 15.3 to make a five-number summary of the sample means.

Did you get the summary (1.5, 4.0, 5.0, 6.0, 8.75)? The median is identical with the population mean and the summary confirms that at least half the sample means lie between 4 and 6. Be sure you understand why.

This example shows that some of these small samples do not give accurate estimates of the population mean. However, a great deal of statistical theory exists about samples and it is possible to make statements of a probabilistic nature about how close a sample mean might be expected to be to the population mean. The setting up and interpretation of such statements is beyond the scope of this book, but a number of statistical texts deal adequately with this problem. See, for example, Yates (1981) or Cochran (1977).

Intuitively it seems we should get a better estimate of the sample mean if we take a larger sample.

Exercise 15.3.   Mathematicians have shown that there are only thirty-six different samples of seven that can be formed from nine units. List for each of these thirty-six samples the values for the numbers of alterations on the manuscript pages given in Table 15.1, setting the numbers out in a table analogous to Table 15.2. Calculate the mean – correct to one decimal place – for each sample and arrange them in a frequency table like Table 15.3.

Your table should be like Table 15.4.

Exercise 15.4.   Form a five-number summary of the sample means in Table 15.4.

Does your summary read (3.6, 4.6, 5.0, 5.5, 6.3)? Clearly the estimates, as we would intuitively expect, cluster more closely round

Table 15.4. *Frequency table of means*
for thirty-six samples of seven
from nine items

Mean	Frequency	Per cent of total
3.6	1	2.8
3.7	1	2.8
3.9	1	2.8
4.0	1	2.8
4.1	1	2.8
4.3	2	5.6
4.4	1	2.8
4.6	2	5.6
4.7	3	8.3
4.9	4	11.1
5.0	3	8.3
5.1	3	8.3
5.3	2	5.6
5.4	2	5.6
5.6	1	2.8
5.7	2	5.6
5.9	2	5.6
6.0	2	5.6
6.1	1	2.8
6.3	1	2.8
Total	36	100.4

the population mean of five for samples of seven than they did for samples of four. Over half the possible samples, nineteen from thirty-six, give a mean between 4.6 and 5.4, i.e. the correct population value of 5 when rounded to the nearest whole number. Also, rounded to the nearest integer, any sample mean lies between four and six.

Exercise 15.5. For both the cases, all possible samples of four, and all possible samples of seven, from a population of nine calculate the mean of all sample means. To get an accurate result for samples of seven you will in effect have to keep more decimal places in your calculation than the one decimal place given in Table 15.4. Indeed think how you might arrange your calculation to avoid any round-off in the mean of all sample means of seven. There is a hint on p. 283 if you are stumped.

A remarkable feature of your answer to Exercise 15.5 – if your calculations are correct – is that in both cases the mean of all means is exactly five – the population mean. This is a demonstration of a mathematical theorem that tells us much more generally that if we form *all* samples of size *n* from a population of larger size *N*, then the mean of all the sample means is equal to the population mean. Statisticians call this property *unbiasedness*.

The information in Tables 15.3 and 15.4 is presented graphically in Figure 15.1(a) and (b). Note the useful device of two vertical scales in that figure. On the left we give a scale of percentages and on the right total numbers. This device is particularly useful here. The left-hand scale is the same for each figure. The right-hand scales then necessarily differ because of the differing sample sizes.

As we expected intuitively, our samples have shown that the larger the sample the better the estimate of the population mean. Our estimates were not very reliable with a sample of four from nine – less than 50 per cent of the population. With a sample of seven from nine – nearly 80 per cent of the population – our estimates were quite good.

This seems to imply that our sample must be a high proportion of the population to give good results. Random sampling would not be useful if this were so, for little effort would be saved compared to looking at the whole population.

Unless the population is very small (when we are more likely to use a census than a sample survey) the accuracy with which we determine a mean (or any other population characteristic) depends almost entirely on the sample size and only to a very limited extent upon the size of the population. Had our population been 100 or 10 000 pages of manuscript rather than nine, but with much the same spread of alterations, i.e. a fairly even spread of between zero and about a dozen alterations per page, then taking samples of seven from 100 pages would have given results very similar to taking samples of seven from 10 000 pages. In neither case would they be quite as good as samples of seven from nine, for nine is not much bigger than seven.

It would be a major task to form every sample of size seven from a population of 100, for there are in all 16 007 560 800 possible samples! Here theory, beyond the scope of this book, comes to our aid.

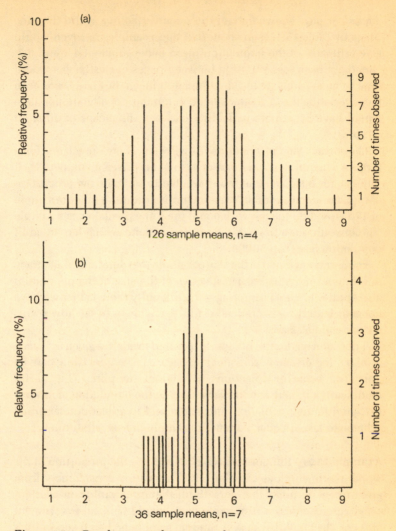

Figure 15.1. Random sample means when N = 9, n = 4, 7.]

How accurate the mean of a sample of size *n* is as an estimate of the population mean will depend chiefly upon the variability in the population and the size of the sample. It can be shown that if we had a population of 100 manuscript pages and the numbers of alterations per page showed about the same variability as did the nine pages in Table 15.1, then about half these samples of seven would give estimates of the population mean between about 4.3 and 5.7. Had there been less variation between pages our estimates would tend to be even closer to the population mean, but had there been more variation (i.e. a greater spread in numbers of alterations) there would have been more variability between the means of different samples.

The virtual lack of relationship between N and precision for a given n when n is small compared to N surprises many people. It implies, for instance, that if one wanted to estimate the proportion of smokers among London's several million adults a random sample of 100 would do the job with about the same precision as a sample of 100 would for a town like Perth in Scotland which has an adult population less than 50 000.

The argument that it is the size of sample that determines accuracy of estimates more or less irrespective of the size of the population also applies to quota sampling – the difficulty there is that we have not got a battery of theoretical results to enable us to say how accurate our estimates are.

A decision on the size of sample required to attain a given accuracy is a matter of some statistical expertise. The precision can be improved using modifications of random sampling. One useful modification if there is wide variability in the population of interest is to divide the population into *strata* and to adjust our sampling scheme to take, in effect, a random sample in each stratum.

Example 15.2. Suppose we wish to estimate the proportion of the workforce unemployed in the UK. This varies considerably from area to area. We might therefore divide the country into non-overlapping regions or strata (a suitable basis would be local government areas or electoral districts). A random sample is then taken in each area, the results being combined according to specified rules to give a figure for the whole country. Details of what size sample to take in total and from each stratum and how to combine the results are beyond the scope of this book.

The idea of stratification has similarities to quota sampling where an attempt is made to allow for various characteristics or strata; an important difference is that in stratified random sampling the actual respondents are chosen at random — not just left to the whims of an interviewer to select his sample to comply with a certain pre-specified total for each stratum. The need for pre-selection of the actual units and then locating and interviewing each, or sending a questionnaire to each, is one of the factors that increase the cost of random as opposed to quota sampling.

Nearly random samples

Example 15.3.   Because of technical difficulties in selecting a truly random sample, methods are sometimes used that it is believed will effectively give a random sample. For example if we have an electorate with 27 300 electors and want a sample of 250 electors this implies that about one in each 109 electors will be required for the sample. On the register the names will probably be arranged alphabetically for the whole region or at least within sub-districts in the electorate. If, instead of taking a random sample, we took every 109th name on the register starting at a randomly selected number between 1 and 109 we get a sample that is often referred to as a *pseudo-random sample*. If the question put is, for example, about voting intentions, this sample should behave very like a random sample, for there is no reason to suppose that order in an alphabetically arranged register would influence voting intentions.

Example 15.4.   In other situations there may be a danger in using pseudo-random or systematic samples of this type. For example, in a survey on household expenditure on a housing estate, if it were decided to take every tenth house in a number of streets, then if the estate has a fairly uniform layout it could turn out that every tenth house was a corner house which is larger than others and will therefore be occupied by bigger or wealthier families than those on the rest of the estate. This may give a bias in that the families in these larger houses may well have a different expenditure pattern (or be larger families) than those in the humbler abodes forming the rest of the estate. Alternatively, taking every tenth house may result in the sample excluding all corner houses so that these larger houses are not represented at all.

Some sampling pitfalls

It is worthwhile drawing attention to some more pitfalls. We have already mentioned on page 183 the importance of asking the right questions. Most sampling that involves collecting information about humans or their activities requires either interviews or the filling in of questionnaires. Both methods tend to be a costly way of gathering information and sometimes corners are cut to save cost. This can cause trouble.

Example 15.5. Suppose a survey of families in a city is made to determine patterns of expenditure on food and clothing. It is decided to use a quota sample but to save interviewing time information is collected by telephone calls. Immediately this implies that the results can only apply to a population of telephone subscribers and their expenditure patterns may well be different from those of families (probably composed largely of the poor and the elderly) who do not have telephones. Even if a random or stratified random sample of telephone subscribers were used these limitations would still apply. We would be taking a sample of all telephone owners and *not* one of the entire population of the city.

A classic example of this pitfall was a newspaper 'telephone straw poll' many years ago in the US that predicted a Republican victory. The Democrats won. At that time a higher proportion of Republican supporters owned telephones.

Example 15.6. Another way of saving interviewing time is by sending out postal questionnaires. Here the problem is non-response. In practice a 50 per cent response is reasonable. A 70 per cent response is generally regarded as good, indeed exceptional, where there is no compulsion or incentive (e.g. a free prize) to make one co-operate. Are the 70 per cent who respond typical of the whole population? May not non-respondents be people who have a vested interest in not replying? For example, if the questionnaire is sent out by a government agency and asks about income, non-response may be tied to fears that information would reach the Inland Revenue and people who have this fear – such as tax dodgers – may be atypical of the population as a whole.

Example 15.7. To avoid sampling large areas or having to make use of large sampling frames a method known as cluster sampling is sometimes used. Well-defined *clusters* of units are selected at random and then samples taken within clusters. One must take care that the selection of clusters does not introduce a bias. For example, if it is decided to select only people whose surnames begin with five chosen letters of the alphabet a random choice of the five letters may include the letter M. This will give a high proportion of people with Scottish ancestry with names beginning in M', Mac, Mc. Similarly the Os include a high proportion with Irish ancestry. Ancestry may influence answers to questions, especially those of a political or patriotic nature.

Some important UK surveys

On page 172 we explained that calculation of the Retail Price Index uses information on family expenditure gleaned from the annual *Family Expenditure Survey*. The units in this survey are *households*. A household is defined as all who live at the same address and share common catering facilities, but excludes hotels, hostels and boarding houses. There is no implication of a blood or marriage relationship between members; domestic servants are included. While family homes or flats are obviously included, groups with looser associations such as students or workers sharing a flat also qualify. To conduct the survey some 11 000 addresses are selected annually, although the precise basis of selection is not made clear in the brief description given in the 'Definitions' and 'Explanatory Notes' to the *Monthly Digest of Statistics*. Effectively this leads to about 10 400 families.

Exercise 15.6. Why do you think 11 000 addresses only produce a sample of about 10 400 families?

It is reported that about 70 per cent co-operate and fill in the questionnaire. There is a danger of a non-response bias here. Caution should also be exercised when comparing year-to-year results as definitions vary slightly, the survey being designed for information relevant to calculating the RPI. Careful definitions of income and expenditure are needed to get meaningful and comparable results from all respondents. For example, income is gross before deduction of tax and national insurance contributions but excludes proceeds from sale of cars or other capital assets, legacies, insurance policy maturity proceeds, windfalls and most in-kind payments (use of company cars, free suits, etc.). On the expenditure side outlay on goods and services *excludes* savings and investment, income tax and national insurance payments, mortgages and other costs for purchase of and additions or extensions to a house. There are special provisions for hire purchase and credit finance. What housing expenditure is included depends on the type of accommodation but rent, rates and insurance are covered. Persons classified as *working* include temporary absentees from work and the unemployed and the self-employed.

The tax and prices index makes substantial use of the Inland Revenue *Survey of Personal Incomes*. Here the unit is the 'tax unit' consisting of a single person or married couple. This choice is a reflection of the illogical basis of the UK tax system rather than a whim of those conducting the survey. The survey covers a stratified sample of 37 500 tax units. The estimated gross income and tax liability of each unit in a given year provides a basis for calculation of the TPI (see p. 175).

Sample size and accuracy

We noted that the sample size in the *Family Expenditure Survey* is just over 10 000 (with an effective response of some 7000) and for the *Survey of Personal Incomes* it is 37 500 units. Providing the selection basis is sensible and steps are taken to avoid bias either by sensible quota choice or by proper random or effectively random methods, samples of this size should be extremely accurate. The theory exists for random samples to tell us what size sample is needed to estimate any population characteristic to any required degree of accuracy. Intuitively, as mentioned on page 197, we expect this to depend upon how variable the characteristic is in the population – the more variable the characteristic the larger the sample we need to estimate it with a given degree of accuracy. Since most surveys are interested in gaining information on several characteristics, some of which will show more variability than others, it follows that with a fixed sample size different characteristics will be estimated with different accuracy.

We must stress that the detail of how to select an appropriate sample to answer a specific question about a population with a required degree of accuracy is a matter of getting sound statistical advice – preferably from a statistician with a good knowledge of using sampling methods to glean information.

Properly used, sampling methods tell us a lot about population characteristics. To illustrate the degree of accuracy, if a random sample of 1000 adult Londoners indicates that 43 per cent are smokers, then in the adult population of London as a whole it is virtually certain (in the sense that there is only about one chance in 100 that it is wrong) that the following statement is true. *The proportion of adults in London who smoke lies between 39 and 47 per cent.* If we took a sample of 10000 these limits would reduce to *between 41.7 and 44.3 per cent* if the sample again indicated a 43 per cent proportion. A well-planned quota sample or stratified random sample could be expected to do appreciably better.

Acceptance sampling

When a buyer is purchasing a large batch of goods he wants to be reasonably sure the quality is up to specification. In an imperfect world it is unlikely that every item in a mass-produced batch of 10000 items will be perfect. It may be prohibitively costly to ensure perfection by complete testing. It would of course be impractical to test every item if the test were destructive by nature. For example, if the items were light bulbs and the specification were that 99 per cent should burn at least 1000 hours, it is self-defeating to test each unit to see how long it burns before failure.

In either situation some protection is available from sampling schemes. A typical scheme for a purchase of 10 000 identical items might be to take a random sample of 100 and accept the whole batch if none or one only are faulty. Otherwise the batch is rejected.

Generally speaking, the higher the proportion of faulty items in the population (whole batch) the higher the proportion of faulty items in the sample. Conversely, a high proportion of faulty items in the sample implies a high proportion in the population.

The odds on accepting a batch with various proportions faulty using any specified sampling scheme can be calculated. The scheme used is selected so that the probability of accepting, on the basis of the sampling results, a batch with an unacceptably high number of defectives is very small.

There are a number of variants of the above sample scheme. If the sampling is non-destructive then sometimes when a batch is rejected every item in that batch is inspected and the faulty ones are removed. A number of schemes are discussed by Wetherill (1977).

16 Experiments and inference

Why experiment?

Surveys tell a lot about the status quo in any population; but what if we want to find the effect on rate of growth of adding a new hormone to pig food, or the consequences of changing the proportions of two metals in an alloy? We then disturb the status quo! It's best to do an experiment.

In the pig example, ideally we might want to know how the hormone will affect the growth of pigs of different breeds at various stages of growth in, say, the United Kingdom, in the United States, in the whole of Western Europe, in the USSR, in Tanzania and in Australia. In theory one could take a random or representative sample from all pigs in the world and try the new hormone on them. This may not please the farmers whose pigs are selected. Also, the cost of supplying the hormone, supervising its feeding to pigs scattered throughout the world and recording the measurements necessary to ascertain its effectiveness becomes virtually impossible. Further, to get an indication of how much the hormone improves growth, we would need information about the rate at which pigs grew without it. To get this we would need a second sample of pigs not treated with hormone, but otherwise comparable to the first sample.

In practice we can get useful information more easily and cheaply by carrying out a planned experiment, using pigs from available sources.

Planning an experiment

We plan any experiment to take into account, so far as resources will allow, all factors that interest us.

Example 16.1. Continuing with the pig example, we may want to know not only whether the new hormone has an effect but also if the effect is greater with some breeds than others; so we might decide to include pigs of the three most important breeds in the regions of interest to us. We may suspect the hormone will react differently if the pigs are normally fed on non-identical diets and so decide to feed pigs of each breed in the experiment on four different basic diets. We may also want to compare growth at, say, four different levels of hormone. To give a baseline, or yardstick, we will need to include pigs of each breed on each diet *without* added hormone. This we can regard as an additional zero level of hormone – *control* is the experimenter's jargon – thus giving five hormone levels in all.

So we end up with wanting to test five hormone levels on pigs of three different breeds, with four different basic feeds. This is easily seen to give $5 \times 3 \times 4 = 60$ different combinations of the *factors* (hormone level, breed, diet) we wish to compare. Thus we need sixty pigs to test each factor level on one pig.

Our prime aim in the experiment will be to see which factors are important in giving the best commercial results. We may have secondary aims, such as making sure there are no harmful side-effects. It is no good having pigs growing twice as fast if the meat is tainted by the hormone when it gets to market – or if people who eat bacon from treated pigs experience a sex change!

Replication

Trying each factor combination on only one pig might be misleading if we are interested in the general effect of widespread use of the treatment. Pigs have individuality; a sample of one is too small! With the same diet and hormone level it is unlikely that any two pigs of the same breed would respond in exactly the same way. Thus, in practice, to get meaningful results we need to test each factor combination on more than one pig. Just how often we can test each combination may be restricted by the number of pigs available or by our financial resources, but experts can *design* an experiment of this type and conduct it in a way that gives quite illuminating results if each factor combination is applied to quite small numbers of animals – say three, four or five. The number of experimental units (the unit is here a pig) on which we repeat each factor combination is called the *replication*. If each factor combination is applied to four pigs, we have four replicates, or four-fold replication. With sixty factor combinations a four-replicate experiment would require $60 \times 4 = 240$ pigs.

Conducting the experiment

An experiment of this size is not cheap to carry out and involves hard and exacting work. Pigs receiving different diets will have to be fed separately. It may be necessary to feed identical diets separately to each breed, for if the pigs of one breed are more aggressive than those of the other breeds, the aggressive pigs may get more than their share of the diet and starve the other pigs. Weight of each pig will have to be recorded at regular intervals to establish and compare growth patterns for each of the sixty factor combinations. Pre-planning is needed. Which pigs of each breed are to receive which diet and hormone level? What records are to be taken? How is data to be recorded? What precautions are needed to minimize and detect errors?

The experiment completed, the records must be analysed statistically to predict how the hormone will affect growth rates for various diets or breeds, i.e. to answer the questions of interest. Is the hormone any use? What is the best level? Is it more effective with some breeds or diets than others?

Analysing results

The aim of the statistical analysis is to predict from the experimental results what will happen in hypothetical populations of pigs of a certain breed fed on a particular diet with a certain level of added hormone. Using the experimental results the statistician does something not unlike making predictions about a population on the basis of observations on a sample.

Earlier, at the planning stage the statistician can give useful advice

about how to extract the maximum relevant information from
experiments of this type.

Ideally, we hope our experiment would tell us something like this:
if we feed diet D to pigs of breed B with an amount X of added
hormone we will get on average a P per cent weight increase over
a ten-week growing period with no adverse effects, and for some
particular D, B and X this P is better than we would get with any
other combination of diet and hormone with this or any other breed
tested in the experiment.

The statistical analysis is sophisticated. In it we compare very
small samples (with four replicates, samples of four) representing
each factor combination. We make inferences from these samples
about the hypothetical population of all pigs of a particular breed
raised on a given diet at a specified hormone level.

The samples are highly selected. The pigs will often be some
raised in the rather special conditions of an experimental agricultural station or else have been provided by farmers who voluntarily
co-operate in experiments. Such farmers are often the more enlight-
ened of their fraternity and therefore the animals they provide may
be more carefully bred and better looked after than those of the
average farmer. Indeed in the field of agriculture it is common to
find that experiments paint too rosy a picture. Nevertheless, they
usually give a reliable *comparative* ordering of the responses to
different factor combinations and are the key method for getting
information about new materials or new techniques not only in agriculture or animal husbandry but in biological sciences generally.
Experiments are also important in studying the effect of changes in
industrial processes, and perhaps most important of all in testing
treatments in medicine. How to set up the best experiment and how
to analyse the results to find out what we can about populations is
a matter for statistical expertise. It has very important implications
in the general field of data collection and data handling.

The statistical viewpoint

This book does not aim to teach statistics, but anyone
collecting data or conducting scientific experiments should have a

feeling for the sort of inferences one might reasonably make. It helps if, without striving for statistical expertise, one has a broad idea about how the statistician looks at data to draw inferences in very simple cases.

To help you attain this we illustrate statistical reasoning with heuristic accounts of one or two standard but very simple statistical analyses. This will not turn you into a statistician, but will, I hope, give you the flavour of how the statistician works with data and help you to appreciate the value (and limitations) of statistical thinking.

A simple statistical test

Example 16.2. Suppose an alloy is normally produced at a temperature of 315°C, but the manufacturers are anxious to reduce fuel costs by making it at a temperature of 290°C. The important property that must be retained is its hardness. This is measured by a hardness tester – an instrument which registers in arbitrary units the force needed to produce a 'dent' of given size.

It is known that even at 315° there are variations in hardness from batch to batch depending on the source of raw material and other factors in the process – accuracy of mixing the proportions, etc. Also within any one batch there is variation from sample to sample.

To compare the effect of reducing temperature while other conditions are kept as similar as possible, a mix of the ingredients is made and divided into twenty-one portions, one such portion being placed into each of the twenty-one furnaces operated at the plant. Ten of these are operated at the normal temperature of 315° and the remaining eleven at the new temperature of 290°. In case the positioning of the furnaces has any effect on hardness, a sensible precaution is to select at random the ten furnaces to be operated at the higher temperature, and the remaining eleven are operated at the lower temperature. A full explanation of why this is desirable would run to many pages. In this particular example it may not affect our conclusions but it does minimize the risk of the experimenter – consciously or even accidentally – giving more favourable circumstances to one experimental situation.

The hardness is measured on one sample of the alloy produced in

Table 16.1.   *Hardness of samples of*
           alloy made at two temperatures

Temperature	Hardness										
290	31	33	32	31	29	32	33	34	31	34	32
315	34	35	33	32	31	34	36	32	33	35	

each furnace. Measurements of hardness in arbitrary units are given in Table 16.1.

Look carefully at this data. Hardnesses at the lower temperature range from 29 to 34, while at the higher temperature they range from 31 to 36. What about the means?

Exercise 16.1.   From the data in Table 16.1 calculate the mean hardness at each temperature.

The answers you should get are 32 and 33.5. Do you think we should conclude that we get 'on the whole' a harder alloy at the higher temperature? There seems to be evidence pointing that way; the range for the higher temperature is pushed up two points at each end: lowest values 29 and 31 respectively, highest values 34 and 36 respectively.

This evidence is partly counteracted by there being a fair overlap in values. Values between 31 and 34 are in a sector of the range common to both temperatures. In this common sector there are ten of the values at the lower temperature and seven of the values at the higher temperature.

For policy decision making a more detailed analysis is required. A simple thing to do statistically is to argue this way. Here we have samples of eleven and ten units respectively which we hope reflect the long-run behaviour of two hypothetical populations of all the specimens of alloy we will produce and market, one population corresponding to each temperature. Hopefully the sample means are near the population means. In the last chapter we saw that in taking samples from real populations the sample mean did not in general equal the population mean, being sometimes a bit above, sometimes a bit below. We ask: Is the difference between the two sample means sufficient for us to conclude that the samples come from populations with different means, or is the difference in sample means of the order of magnitude we might readily expect in two samples from the same population?

Remember that we pointed out in Chapter 15 (p. 197) that the greater the variability of a characteristic in a population the more the sample mean may vary from one sample to another.

Formulating a hypothesis

Formally, we ask the question: *Is it reasonable to suppose these samples come from the same (hypothetical) population?* If it is, this implies a lack of evidence of an effect of temperature upon hardness. Our test of reasonableness of a *hypothesis* that the samples come from the same population is based on the answer to the question: If the hypothesis is true, what is the probability, given the variability between individual observations that we have in our samples, that we would get as large or a larger difference in magnitude between the sample means? If this probability is small we reject the hypothesis that the population means are the same.

The above is a crude outline of the problem. The technicalities of how the statistician makes a decision depend upon what further assumptions he is prepared to make. One common assumption is that the sample values come from what is called a *normal distribution.* 'Normal' here is a piece of statistical jargon and carries no implication that there is anything abnormal if they do not follow this distribution. We say more about this distribution in Chapter 17. We suppose he is prepared to make the assumption here. The statistician then calculates a ratio with numerator being the difference between the means and denominator a measure of spread that is closely associated with *standard deviation* (p. 77). This ratio is usually denoted by t. Intuitively it is clear that if the population means differ, then the sample means are likely to show a greater difference than they would if the two samples came from the same population. Clearly, for a fixed value of the measure of spread (the denominator), the ratio t will increase as the difference between the sample means increases.

Testing a hypothesis

Statisticians are able to calculate the probability that t takes a value with magnitude as great or greater than a value we obtain for our data *if* the samples came from identical populations. If this probability is small it suggests the populations have different means. We then say we reject the hypothesis that the populations are the same. A piece of statistical jargon describes the result as *significant*, when we reject the hypothesis.

To calculate the measure of variability that forms the denominator in t, we first work out for each sample separately the sum of squares of deviations from its mean (steps 1 to 3 on p. 79). We then add our two results and divide by *two less* than the total number of observations in the samples, i.e. in our case by $21 - 2 = 19$. We now multiply our result by the sum of the reciprocals of the numbers of observations in each of the samples (i.e. by $(1/11 + 1/10)$). Next we take the square root, denoting the result by s_d. This is the measure of variability used in t. All this sounds a mouthful but where possible I am avoiding algebra. We show how this sort of instruction may be expressed algebraically in Appendix C.

Exercise 16.2. Calculate the measure of variability for the data in Table 16.1. Try this on your own, but if you have difficulty we outline the steps below.

We need first the sum of squares of the hardnesses of the samples produced at $290°$, i.e. $31^2 + 33^2 + \ldots + 34^2 + 32^2 = 11\,286$. From this we subtract the square of the total divided by the number of observations, i.e. $352^2/11 = 11\,264$. Thus the sum of squares of deviations, S_1 say, is $S_1 = 11\,286 - 11\,264 = 22$. For the sample of ten at $315°$ similar calculations give the sum of squares of deviations, S_2 say, as $S_2 = 22.5$.

To form s_d (see above) we add S_1 and S_2, divide the result by 19, then multiply by $(1/11 + 1/10)$, and take the square root of the result. Carry out these steps and verify that s_d is given by $s_d = 0.67$ (to two decimal places).

Next we calculate the ratio t of the difference between the samples means, i.e. $33.5 - 32 = 1.5$, to $s_d = 0.67$.

$$\text{i.e. } t = \frac{\text{difference between means}}{s_d} = 1.5/0.67 = 2.24.$$

To decide if this value of t is large enough to indicate whether we should reject the hypothesis that the samples are from the same population the statistician consults a table called a t-table.

From the appropriate table he finds that the probability of getting $t = 2.24$ or a greater value if we took two samples of ten and eleven units from the same normal population is less than 0.05, which means there is less than one chance in twenty of getting this difference if the samples are from the same population.

What are we to infer? Since our high value of t has a low probability of occurring *if the samples are from the same population* it seems reasonable to conclude that a more likely explanation is that the two populations differ, or more specifically our test is designed to see whether it is likely they differ in means. In statistical jargon if we get a t-value which has less than a one-in-twenty chance of occurring when the population means are the same we say our result is *significant at the one-in-twenty level.* This is a numerical measure of the strength of the evidence against the hypothesis that the samples are from the same population. It seems more likely that the hardness really is different *on average* for the alloy made at the lower temperature. In practice we usually do not reject the hypothesis of equal means if our t-value has a probability *greater* than one in twenty of occurring when the samples come from the same population.

Confidence intervals

The above is a sketchy outline of the statistical technique known as hypothesis testing. We have skated over details and dodged vexed questions about what are called one- and two-tail tests. A weakness of hypothesis testing is that a significant result does not necessarily imply the difference is of practical importance! Conversely, a difference of practical importance may not always be classed as significant! Of more general use are statements, which can be made, of the form *with a high (and specified) degree of confidence we believe the difference in mean hardness lies between certain limits L and U.*

We shall not go into details about how such statements are constructed – if you have had some statistical training you will know the procedure is called setting up a *confidence interval*, but some care is needed in using and interpreting such intervals, so if you feel the need for statements of this kind and have not been trained to form or interpret them you'd be well advised to consult a statistician.

The effect of sample size

For a given denominator value s_d the value of t increases as the difference in sample means (the numerator) increases. Large differences in sample means reflect a stronger likelihood that the population means differ. Just how large a difference is needed depends upon the variability as measured by s_d. Theory indicates that s_d generally becomes smaller as we increase the sample sizes. One consequence is that with large samples it is easier to detect smaller differences between population means than can be detected with small samples. It is also possible to pinpoint more closely (the confidence intervals becoming shorter) the likely magnitude of any real difference if the samples are larger.

Pocket calculator standard deviations

We mentioned on page 80 that some pocket calculators 'programmed' to calculate a standard deviation of n observations divide the sum of squares of deviations by $n - 1$ rather than n. They do this because it gives a more direct way of calculating denominators in t. Using our notation S_1, S_2, for the sums of squares of deviations from their respective sample means it is not difficult to see that adding these and dividing by two less than the number of observations is equivalent to taking a *weighted mean* of the variances (i.e. squares of the standard deviations) for each sample providing these variances are calculated by dividing S_1, S_2 by *one less than the number of observations* in each sample. The weights are respectively *one less* than the numbers in each sample.

In many statistical applications *variance* defined with a divisor

$n - 1$ rather than $\dot{n}$ is appropriate, as it gives a better approximation to, or estimate of, the generally unknown variance of the population from which our sample is supposed to be taken.

Further reading

A very detailed account of statistical theory and practice as applied to agricultural experiments is given by Pearce (1983). A general account of the principles of experimentation is given by Cox (1958), and a classic work on industrial experiments is that of Davies (1956); Pocock (1983) discusses clinical experiments.

17 *Statistical tests*

The normal distribution

In testing whether temperature affected hardness (p. 211) one assumption we made was that hardness in a 'population' followed what we called a *normal distribution*.

In very simple terms for metal hardnesses this would be approximately true if, for large samples, a histogram of the observed values based on data grouped into a large number of short intervals (i.e. short relative to the total range of the data) looked something like Figure 17.1.

For this data we easily see the mean (also the median) is very close to the middle value; small deviations from the mean are more common than larger deviations and for any two intervals equidistant

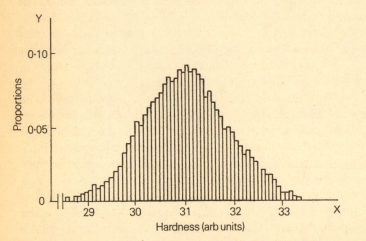

Figure 17.1. Histogram for a large sample of metal hardnesses which follow a normal distribution.

from the mean, one above it and one below it, there are appproximately the same number of observations (i.e. the heights of rectangles equidistant from the mean are much the same). This implies symmetry.

Further, if we calculated the standard deviation (see p. 79) for all our observations we would find for a large sample that about two-thirds of the observations lie in a range from one standard deviation below the mean to one standard deviation above the mean and also that about 95 per cent of them lie within two standard deviations on either side of the mean.

The distribution, a complete study of which requires advanced mathematics, was explored in detail by the celebrated mathematician Gauss at the beginning of the last century, although it was known to earlier mathematicians. It is sometimes called the *Gaussian* distribution, a name that avoids the connotation of *normal* with its implication that all other distributions are in some way *abnormal*. Much experimental data follows a distribution that is very nearly normal. For example, the heights of eighteen-year-old Caucasian males follow an approximately normal distribution with a specified mean and variance (or standard deviation). The values of the mean and variance will depend upon the units (metres, centimetres, inches, or whatever) in which the height is measured. Heights of eighteen-year-old Caucasian females would also be normally distributed, but the mean would be lower than that for males and the variance perhaps also slightly lower. A similar situation holds for many other ethnic groups, the means and standard deviations of heights differing slightly from race to race.

When there are small irregular variations of an unpredictable nature in a measured characteristic (such as variations in the weight of bricks produced in a certain kiln, or the hardnesses of alloys produced at a fixed temperature) we commonly find our data following an approximately normal distribution. There are sound theoretical reasons why this should be so.

There is also a lot of data that does not follow a normal distribution and statistical analysis of such data should not in general be based on methods that are highly dependent on the so-called *normality* assumption. For example, the times machines of a certain type run before they break down often do not follow a normal distribution;

some components break down earlier than would be predicted under normal distribution theory whilst others have much longer lives than expected under that theory.

A wide class of methods known as *non-parametric methods* may be more appropriate if we cannot assume normality. Practical aspects of these are described in some detail in the author's *Quick Statistics* (1981).

Another statistical test

When we toss a coin we expect in the *long run* roughly equal numbers of heads and tails. In a short run there will be irregularities. Three heads, or three tails, in three tosses is not surprising, although rather more frequently the result is one head and two tails or two heads and one tail. Toss a coin ten times and four heads and six tails, or even three heads and seven tails, will not be very surprising; but ten heads and no tails would, I think, have you looking to see if the coin were a double header. How do we decide on the basis of a sequence of tosses whether a coin is fair?

Example 17.1. In twelve tosses of a coin you should not be too surprised to get four heads and eight tails. That's twice as many tails as heads. What about forty heads and eighty tails in 120 tosses? I think this would surprise you – yet it is still just twice as many tails as heads; but it does not agree with our experience that in the long run we should get nearly the same number of heads and tails. Ideally we hope for sixty heads and sixty tails in 120 tosses. A discrepancy of one or two from these idealized numbers (statisticians call them the *expected numbers*) is no surprise, but large discrepancies are. How large a discrepancy makes us suspect that a coin is biased? The size of the difference between the *observed* number of heads (or tails) and the expected equal numbers that will alarm us obviously depends to some extent on the size of the expected number.

We allow for this in the appropriate test illustrated in Example 17.2.

Example 17.2. A coin is tossed forty times and heads are observed on sixteen tosses and tails on twenty-four tosses. Is it reasonable to conclude the coin is biased?

If the coin is true we 'expect' twenty heads and twenty tails. If we got that number we would certainly not suspect bias. What we do to test is calculate, both for heads and tails, a ratio which is

$$\frac{(\text{observed number} - \text{expected number})^2}{\text{expected number}}$$

We next add the calculated ratios for heads and tails. In our example for heads the ratio is $(16 - 20)^2/20 = 16/20 = 0.8$. For tails we easily find the ratio also has the value 0.8. Adding these we get the value 1.6 for the sum. Clearly the greater the discrepancy between observed and expected number *for a fixed expected number*, the greater the value of each term making up the sum. Large discrepancies cast doubts about the coin being fair. Tables have been calculated that tell us how big the discrepancy must be before we reject at the one-in-twenty significance level (see p. 213) the hypothesis that the coin is fair. For this example those tables show the required value to be 3.84. As 1.6 is less than 3.84 we accept the hypothesis that the coin is fair. Note again that accepting the hypothesis does not prove the coin is fair. It only says we have insufficient evidence to conclude otherwise.

Exercise 17.1. Suppose that in forty tosses of a coin we observe fourteen heads and twenty-six tails. If we perform calculations analogous to those carried out above, should we now reject the hypothesis that the coin is fair, given that one should do so if the calculated value is greater than 3.84? What if we observe thirteen heads and twenty-seven tails? (Turn to page 284 for help if you have trouble with this exercise.)

In passing we mention that this test is not strictly accurate in the above example; but in practice only if the value obtained on adding the ratio is very close to 3.84, or the expected numbers are very small, are modifications needed.

One test for randomness

In statistical work – selecting random samples is one example – we often require series of *random numbers*. Computers often supply allegedly random digits (the whole numbers 0, 1, 2, 3, 4, 5, 6, 7, 8, 9) using what are called *pseudo-random number generators*. If digits are random an important property they have is that knowing any digit in the sequence is of no help for predicting anything about the next digit – what its value will be, or even if it is more likely to be odd or even, or greater than three or anything else. Conformity to properties like these is not easy to test. Another property of random digits, although not unique to such digits, is that in the long run the numbers of times each of the ten digits 0 to 9 appears should be roughly equal – for each about one-tenth of the total. However, just as in tossing a coin we do not get exactly the same number of heads and tails in a sequence of tosses, we will not usually get equal numbers of occurrences of each digit. The question that arises is how different must they be before we can reasonably reject the hypothesis that our numbers have this essential property of randomness?

Example 17.3. Most computers have a mechanism that produces so-called random numbers. These are strictly termed *pseudo-random numbers* because they are not produced by a method that can be *proved* to give random digits. These procedures have been shown, by testing, to produce digits with all the known properties of random numbers. At least ideally that is what should happen. Unfortunately some computer pseudo-random number generators do not do the job very well. I am writing this book on a word processor that also doubles as a computer. It has a so-called random number generator as part of its software. I used it to generate 200 random digits and counted the number of times each digit occurred. These are given in Table 17.1. Is there evidence the generator is not producing truly random digits?

The 'expected' frequency of each of the ten digits in a random sequence of 200 is twenty. We have got only seven twos instead of the expected twenty. This is the most 'way out' result in this set and makes one suspect the generator is not doing a good job. We use

Table 17.1. *Occurrence frequency of each digit*
           in sequence of 200

Digit	0	1	2	3	4	5	6	7	8	9
Frequency	22	17	7	24	21	24	20	27	16	22

statistical methods to help us test our hunches, proceeding much as we did in the coin-tossing example.

We calculate for each digit the value of

$$\frac{(\text{observed} - \text{expected})^2}{\text{expected}}$$

and add the values obtained. Thus for digit 3, for example, we get $(24 - 20)^2/20 = 16/20 = 0.8$.

Exercise 17.2. Calculate '(observed − expected)²/expected' for each digit in Table 17.1 and add the results.

You should calculate the sum to be 14.2. Note that since the expected number in each case is twenty you can shorten the arithmetic a little by first working out '(observed − expected)²' corresponding to each digit and adding the results, finally dividing the total by twenty.

Having done this we now find in an appropriate table the value that will only be exceeded once in twenty times if the digits are truly random. It turns out to be 16.92. Since we only get a value of 14.2 we have not enough evidence to suppose the digits are not random. This might surprise you after noting that very large deficiency in the frequency of the digit 2 – only seven occurrences compared to an expected twenty.

Exercise 17.3. For further practice here are 150 allegedly random digits from a pocket calculator:

Digit	0	1	2	3	4	5	6	7	8	9
Frequency	13	13	22	20	13	15	13	14	14	13

How do they stand up to our test for randomness? (Your calculated value must again exceed 16.92 to indicate they are not random.)

Although they may survive this test, so-called random numbers may not survive other tests for randomness, but we do not discuss these.

We may extend our example used in Exercise 17.2 to illustrate a statistical point we mentioned before (p. 214) about bigger experiments being better able to pinpoint evidence against a hypothesis.

Exercise 17.4.   Table 17.2 gives the frequency of occurrence of each digit in a sequence of 700 pseudo-random digits from the same generator that produced the results in Table 17.1.

Table 17.2.   *Occurrence frequency of each digit in sequence of 700*

Digit	0	1	2	3	4	5	6	7	8	9
Frequency	48	59	78	77	76	87	60	80	72	63

Here the expected frequency for each digit is 70. Perform calculations analogous to those in Exercise 17.2 to obtain the value of the sum of '(observed − expected)^2/ expected' for each digit. Once again we reject the hypothesis of consistency with the expected values if our answer is greater than 16.92. What do you conclude?

If you agree with my calculations your value should be 18.51. So the evidence casts doubt upon our generator giving equal frequency of digits in the long run.

The fact that we got significance in this case and not in the earlier example where we took only a shorter run of 200 digits is a common phenomenon.

To people brought up in the belief that everything in mathematics is black or white; that propositions (like those met in school geometry) are true or false, this is surprising. In statistics, accepting a hypothesis does not *prove* it is true. Rejecting it does not *prove* it is false. When we reject a hypothesis all we really say is that the evidence against it is very strong. If we do not feel it is strong enough to reject it we continue to accept the hypothesis. In the sense that the data provides the raw evidence as a basis for our test, more data means more evidence.

The distinction between practical importance and statistical significance is important. In many applications a lack of randomness might make random number generators useless – even dangerous, e.g. they are widely used in statistical simulation – a technique which uses a mathematical or statistical model to find out how some physical system works. See e.g. Sprent (1977, pp. 156–63) or Moore (1980, pp. 323–9). It is important before doing this type of work to test a pseudo-random number generator thoroughly. Many of those in standard computer packages are not good. Note that the correct (i.e. approximately equal) long-run frequency of digits is not the only requirement of randomness – we have already mentioned that given any random numbers you must not be able to predict anything about future numbers.

Exercise 17.5. If your generator gave the following output, in order, the frequency of digits would be acceptable – each occurs exactly three times. But there is a pattern. Can you spot it?

1, 6, 3, 8, 5, 4, 7, 2, 9, 0, 3, 8, 7, 6, 1, 4, 9, 0, 5, 2, 5, 0, 3, 8, 1, 6, 7, 4, 9, 2

Exercise 17.6. Use the results of Exercise 4.6 to decide if there is enough evidence to reject the hypothesis that computer breakdowns occur uniformly throughout the working day. Since there are ninety breakdowns spread over sixteen one-hour intervals, uniformity implies an expected number of $90/16 = 5.625$ in each one-hour interval. If you work out '(observed − expected)^2/expected' for each one-hour interval and add you should reject the hypothesis of uniformity if you get a value exceeding 25.

The tests used in Examples 17.1 to 17.3 are called chi-squared (or χ^2) tests, χ being the Greek letter pronounced 'chi'. For further discussion of its uses, with examples, see Sprent (1977, Chapter 3), Sprent (1981, pp. 155–67, 175–85) and Rowntree (1981, pp. 150–4) or nearly any elementary statistics text.

Random arrivals

In Exercise 6.4, p. 80, we showed that for a reasonably large set of data (100 observations) for intervals between cars passing a fixed point on a motorway the mean interval between cars was almost equal to the standard deviation of the intervals, their respective values being 10.94 and 10.27. This is an interesting feature to a statistician. It is an indication that cars are arriving *at random*. By this we mean that the intervals between the arrival of two (or more) cars tell us nothing about when future cars will arrive. All we can assert is that in the long run the average interval between cars will be a little over ten seconds (the mean time). The situation is distinct from one of clumping. If we made our observations not on an open stretch of motorway but in a street where cars approached through traffic lights we would have a clumping situation, and the *mean = standard deviation* (approximately) property would not hold.

Example 17.4. Suppose at a busy intersection the traffic lights hold up vehicles for twenty seconds and then allow them to pass for a further twenty seconds, the cycle being repeated. After the lights turn to green we may expect a number of cars held at the lights to pass within about one second of each other, then perhaps one or two who arrive at the lights when they are green and are not held up will pass at slightly longer intervals, with perhaps four, five or more seconds between them. Then there will be a gap of at least twenty seconds while the lights are again red before further vehicles pass (we assume no vehicles turn in from a side street or jump the lights during this period). The intervals given in Table 17.3 represent the

Table 17.3.   *Interval between vehicles passing a check-point*

1	1	1	1	3	7	2	4	21	1	1	1	1	3	1
3	7	24	1	1	6	2	9	29	1	1	1	1	1	1
3	1	3	7	2	26	2	3	1	1	2	5	1	8	25
1	1	1	2	1	3	1	1	4	7	26	1	1	2	1
3	1	3	6	2	4	24	1	2	2	1	3	1	1	3
5	3	27	1	1	2	2	1	3	1	2	2	6	3	24
2	3	1	1	2	1	11	27	2	1					

sort of pattern we might get observing 100 vehicles in these circumstances.

Exercise 17.7. Calculate the mean and standard deviation of the data in Table 17.3. (Look back to page 79 if you have forgotten how to calculate a variance and standard deviation.) How has the obvious 'clumping' of cars held up at the lights influenced the relationship between mean and standard deviation as compared to that when the flow is random?

If your calculations are correct you will find the standard deviation is roughly half as big again as the mean (the precise values are given on p. 284). This is typical of the effect of clumping.

Example 17.5. A common danger is to jump to conclusions based on too little data. It is often tempting to do so. For example suppose a new drug is being tried to cure a rare disease. Only twenty-two patients are available. It is decided to allocate ten of these to the best-known standard cure and the remaining twelve to the new cure, with the results summarized in Table 17.4.

Table 17.4.   *Patient responses to*
         a drug

	Successes	Failures
Standard drug	3	7
New drug	7	5

Given this data instinct tells us the evidence is strong that the new drug is superior. In fact the statistical evidence is not strong. Look at it this way. Suppose the drugs are equally effective so it does not matter which we give a patient. Then, if we were to get, as we have above, among all twenty-two patients a total of ten successes and twelve failures, what is the probability that if we select ten of these at random (corresponding to the ten who get the standard drug) we will get three who are successes and seven who are failures? Look at it this equivalent way. Suppose we have twenty-two cards – ten labelled 'S' for success and twelve labelled 'F' for failure. We put them all in a hat and stir them up well. Now we ask somebody to draw out ten of them. Would you be surprised to get three 'S's and seven 'F's in your draw? I wouldn't. That outcome automatically leaves seven 'S's and five 'F's in the hat (corresponding to the *new* drug patients). This is a situation where more testing is called for before we could decide whether one drug is superior.

Medical research workers have a particularly bad record among scientists for misuse of statistical techniques. One survey of leading medical journals by a competent statistician showed that some half of the papers reporting quantitative results used either inappropriate or inadequate statistical techniques. Fortunately, in many cases they still reached the right conclusion – but by incorrect reasoning! In other cases the conclusions were wrong.

Our aim

Chapters 16 and 17 are not designed to turn you into statisticians. Rather, we have tried to give a peep at how the statistician looks at data. We have referred to the use of tables to decide whether something is significant, but we have left those tables as mathematical black boxes. We have looked at how the statistician formalizes hunches about data – how in simple cases he makes decisions about accepting or rejecting those hunches. Most real-world problems require more sophisticated techniques for statistical analysis – and that is when you should call in the expert.

18 *More about relationships*

Nearly straight lines

Example 18.1. Table 18.1 gives the size of the Bloggs Manufacturing Company workforce on 1 June of each year from 1975 to 1983, also the total number (in thousands) of mechanical backscratchers, the product in which the company specializes, produced each year.

Table 18.1. *Labour force and output records, Bloggs, 1975–1983*

	Labour force	Output (thousands)
1975	42	12
1976	56	17
1977	62	21
1978	54	17
1979	31	7
1980	36	10
1981	44	13
1982	51	16
1983	41	12

Exercise 18.1. Study Table 18.1. What general information does it give about Bloggs' output? Can you see any trend with time for labour force or output? Does output appear to be related to the size of the labour force?

A quick inspection shows that both labour force and output change from year to year rather erratically. However, if we look at the labour force in relation to output, not surprisingly output does increase as the labour force expands and decreases as it contracts. The pattern of the relationship is well illustrated by the scatter

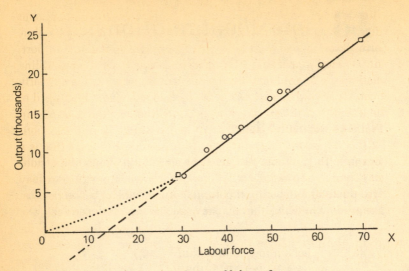

Figure 18.1. Bloggs' output and size of labour force

diagram, Figure 18.1, with production (y) plotted against labour force (x).

The scatter plot shows a nearly straight-line relationship between x and y. It is easy to draw by eye a line that fits these points quite well. This is done in Figure 18.1. Why do this? Because it is a pictorial aid that tells us what is happening in broad terms. Note that two squares have been marked on the line at the points whose co-ordinates are (x = 30, y = 7) and (x = 70, y = 23). This helps us to get quickly an estimate of how much we might reasonably expect production to increase for each additional man employed. We reason this way: If we increase the labour force from thirty to seventy we increase production from seven to twenty-three. In other words, increasing the labour force by $70 - 30 = 40$ increases production by $23 - 7 = 16$. By simple proportions increasing the labour force by one increases production by $16/40 = 0.4$.

A production unit is one thousand backscratchers, so this means 400 backscratchers for every extra man employed. The line also tells us roughly the production we might expect for any given size labour force *within the range of the observations*. For example we see that with a labour force of fifty we would expect a production of about fifteen (thousand) units, i.e. the y co-ordinate of the point on the line corresponding to $x = 50$ is $y = 15$. The phrase in italics is important. Generally speaking it is dangerous to expect a straight-line relationship to hold outwith the range of the observations. Clearly it cannot always do so. Look at the dashed extension downward of the line in Figure 18.1. If we believe this line is a true relationship it tells us that with a workforce of ten we should produce about -2 (i.e. approximately -2000 units per annum)! Clearly this is a nonsense. In mathematical language we say the straight line does not extrapolate downward. A curve such as the dotted curve may give a more realistic picture of production with a smaller workforce. Similarly it would be unwise to extrapolate upward. Increasing the workforce to 100 may not bring the same steady rate of increased production; there may not be enough equipment for 100 men to work at full potential; or if making mechanical backscratchers is highly skilled, there may not be a pool of suitably trained labour to provide additional fully productive operators.

Modern statistical computer packages usually have a program to fit a straight line to paired observations. So do some pocket calculators. Since these machines cannot do things by eye, they use mathematical techniques to fit what is usually called a regression line, or more specifically the *least squares regression line of y on x*.

Regression lines

The regression line fitted by a computer usually has the form $y = a + bx$ where a and b are constants determined from the data. Here is how b is calculated. The flow diagram in Figure 18.2 will help you follow the steps.

If we have data for a set of paired x and y values the computer determines the value of b by first calculating for each pair the product of corresponding x and y values, then adding all these products. From the result we subtract the product of the sums of all the x and y values divided by the number of paired observations to give a number P. The result is divided by the value we get by summing the squares of all x values and subtracting the square of their sum div-

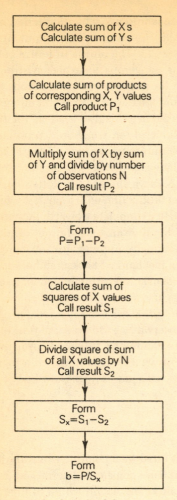

Figure 18.2. Calculation of the constant b in regression.

ided by the number of observations to give a number S_x. It sounds very complicated but perhaps you recognize S_x? It is the sum of squares of deviations of the x values from their mean which we used in calculating the variance in Chapter 6, p. 79. Obtaining P is in fact equivalent to calculating the sums of products of deviations of x and y from their respective means. Once b is calculated a is easily obtained by the formula

$$a = (\text{mean of } y) - b \times (\text{mean of } x).$$

Exercise 18.2. For the data in Table 18.1 find the values of a and b by carrying through the steps outlined below.

For convenience we rewrite the x, y values from Table 18.1 below:

x	42	56	62	54	31	36	44	51	41
y	12	17	21	17	7	10	13	16	12

Verify that the totals of x and y are respectively 417 and 125. Next form the sums of products of corresponding x and y, i.e. $42 \times 12 + 56 \times 17 + 62 \times 21 + \ldots + 41 \times 12$. Verify this has the value 6133. To form the numerator, P, in the expression for b we subtract from this the product of the sums divided by 9, the number of paired values, i.e. $417 \times 125/9 = 5791.67$ to two decimal places. Thus $P = 6133 - 5791.67 = 341.33$.

To get S_x we form the sum of squares of deviations from the mean following steps one to three of the process given in Chapter 6, p. 79. These calculations are the same as those for obtaining the variance except that we omit the final division by n (stage four). The value we get is 814, thus

$$b = \frac{341.33}{814} = 0.42.$$

Now the mean of x is $417/9 = 46.33$ and the mean of y is $125/9 = 13.89$, whence $a = 13.89 - 0.42 \times 46.33 = -5.57$.

Thus the *regression line* has the equation

$$y = -5.57 + 0.42x$$

A more algebraic description of these calculations is given in Appendix C.

The coefficient of x, 0.42, is called the *slope* of the line. In geometric terms it measures the increase in y for unit increase in x. It implies that over the range for which the regression is accurate we would expect for every additional man taken on an increase in output of 0.42. This is, to one decimal place, the same increase 0.4 as we predicted from a line fitted by eye. If you have studied trigonometry it may interest you to know that the value of b in the equation $y = a + bx$ is the tangent of the angle between the line and the direction of the x-axis when we use the same scale on both the x and y axes. The value of a is clearly the value of y when $x = 0$ and gives the point where the line cuts the y-axis. As we have already indicated, this particular straight line can have no meaning for values of x in the vicinity of zero so this value is of less intrinsic interest than that of b.

Abuse of regression

Regression programs in this situation (and in more sophisticated ones where we are interested in relationships between several variables) are among the most widely used *and misused* statistical programs for computers.

Example 18.2. We confine our attention to relations between two variables.

Exercise 18.3. For each of the four data sets given in Table 18.2 calculate the regression equation by the method given

Table 18.2. *Four sets of data for regression calculations*

Set 1					
x = 10	15	20	30	35	40
y = 10	20	30	30	25	20
Set 2					
x = 11	25	32	46		
y = 18.5	22.5	24.5	28.5		
Set 3					
x = 9	26.8	32.2	46		
y = 18	24	23	29		
Set 4					
x = 10	15	20	25	30	35	40
y = 16	20	26	23.5	19	24	29

above, or if you have a computer or micro-computer with a regression package use it to calculate the regression constants.

In each case, rounded to two decimal places the equation is

$$y = 15.36 + 0.29x.$$

The data sets are very different. What do they look like on a scatter diagram? We have plotted them in Figures 18.3(a)–(d), together with the fitted line.

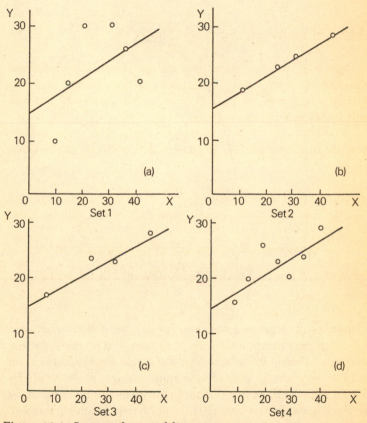

Figure 18.3. Scatter plots and linear regressions for four data sets (Table 18.2).

What about these fits? That in Figure 18.3(b) is perfect, that in Figure 18.3(c) is tolerable. Those in Figures 18.3(a) and 18.3(d) are, to put it mildly, pretty poor. Had you been given just data set one and drawn the scatter diagram would you even have considered trying to fit a straight line to it to indicate trend? Would you not have been happier with something like the freehand curve in Figure 18.4?

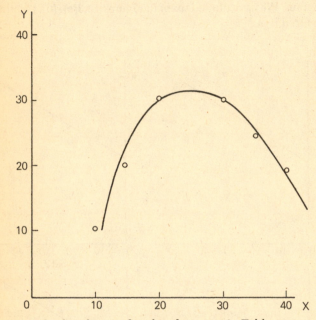

Figure 18.4. A freehand curve fitted to data set 1 in Table 18.2.

These results serve as a warning. For data set one a straight-line fit is completely inappropriate. For data set two it is almost perfect. For data set three it is a tolerable way of giving a general indication based on very limited data of how x and y might relate; while for data set four the line seems rather inadequate; but unlike data set one there is no obvious alternative relationship that might be used.

Most computer programs do provide evidence as to how well a line fits data, but all too often this is misunderstood or ignored.

Its interpretation is quite complicated and help from a statistician should be sought if a scatter plot suggests a straight line is inappropriate.

Correlation

Given a set of paired observations, almost as popular an occupation as fitting a regression line is the calculation of a correlation coefficient. To calculate it we begin as for regression by calculating the sum of products of deviations from the means for x and y and also the sum of squares of deviations of the xs from their mean: P and S_x in Figure 18.2. To get the correlation coefficient we also need the sum of squares of the deviations of the y values from their mean; this we denote S_y. Then the correlation coefficient r is found by dividing P by the square root of the product of S_x and S_y. We may write:

$$r = \frac{P}{\sqrt{(S_x S_y)}}$$

It always has a value between $+1$ and -1. Values of exactly $+1$ or -1 indicate that all the (x,y) points lie on a straight line. If the value is $+1$ the line has a positive slope, i.e. it climbs from left to right across the page. If it has the value -1 it descends from left to right, i.e. the slope is negative. The correlation coefficient does not tell us how steep the slope is.

It is a popular belief that a correlation coefficient with value nearly 1 or nearly -1 implies very nearly a perfect straight-line relationship and a correlation coefficient near zero implies a completely random scatter of points. It is true that if we have a scatter of points like that in Figure 18.5 the correlation coefficient will be near zero, but it may also be near zero in situations where clearly there is some relationship between x and y, but this relationship is not linear.

Example 18.3.   Consider data set one in Table 18.2. In calculating the regression coefficient you will have found that $P = 200$. (If you used a computer program to calculate the regression you may not have this value, but never mind because your computer, if it has a

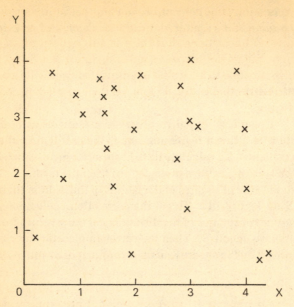

Figure 18.5. One case of zero correlation.

program to calculate regression coefficients, almost certainly also has one to calculate correlation coefficients.) The value of S_x is 700. The value of S_y is easily found to be 287.5. Thus the correlation coefficient is

$$r = \frac{200}{\sqrt{(700 \times 287.5)}} = 0.4458.$$

This does not indicate a very strong linear relationship between x and y, a situation demonstrated in Figure 18.3. However there is a definite curvilinear (i.e. curved line) relationship.

Exercise 18.4.   Consider the data set one in Table 18.2 with the one additional point $x = 45$, $y = 5$. By visualizing this point added in Figure 18.4 verify that it is reasonably consistent with the trend curve shown on that figure. Now calculate the correlation coefficient for data set one plus this additional point.

Did you get the value r = −0.132? If not, see page 284 for details of the calculation. Here then is a case of a small correlation coefficient indicating no linear trend, but there is still a clear curve passing close to the points (its shape is something like a parabola).

It is also possible to have a set of points that clearly lie exactly on some curve other than a straight line, yet their correlation coefficient is nearly one.

Example 18.4.   Table 18.3 gives a small data set of paired values.

Table 18.3.   *A set of paired values*

x	0	1	2	3	4
y	1	2	5	10	17

The correlation coefficient is easily calculated as r = 0.9589. Plotted on a graph these points do not seem to lie too far from a straight line but there is a definite curving tendency. Indeed these points satisfy *exactly* the relationship $y = 1 + x^2$. Check this by substituting in values from Table 18.3. This is the equation to a parabola.

Thus we see that one must not jump to the conclusion that high correlations mean a near straight-line relationship and near zero correlations a nearly complete scatter. Generally speaking a high positive correlation indicates a positive relationship, i.e. x increasing as y increases, and a highly negative correlation (coefficient near −1) indicates a negative relationship, i.e. x decreasing as y increases.

The correlation concept is often associated with a notion of cause and effect. If we increase the labour force we expect increased output – there is a positive correlation between size of labour force and output. But sometimes a positive correlation only reflects dependence on a third factor – often time – with no causal relationship. To pretend there might be is a nonsense. For example, the number of television licences taken out each year in the period 1950–60 correlates highly with the numbers of patients receiving treatment for psychiatric disorders each year. This should not be taken to indicate that people with psychiatric disorders have a special tendency to take out TV licences or that taking out TV licences causes psychiatric disorders.

In other cases, though time may be the common factor that implies an increase in each of two measures, there may well be a natural association. For example, successive measurements of heights and weights of a child as it grows older tend to be correlated, and although the causal factor for both may fundamentally be increasing age, we nevertheless expect an increase in height to produce a greater body weight.

A celebrated correlation established in recent years was that between smoking and lung cancer. The high correlation did not in itself prove a link; it was only when cancer-inducing agents were found – particularly in the tar component – in tobacco, that a link was firmly established.

Where we are comparing a number of factors a pair-wise comparison of correlation coefficients may be illuminating. An interesting example is given by Ehrenberg (1983, pp. 210–11). In this example he shows how high correlations between individuals' time spent viewing certain 'pairs' of TV programmes and low correlations between other pairs indicate a dichotomy of TV audiences. He considers ten leading programmes on British TV – five devoted to sport and five to current affairs. The correlations are high between all pairs of the five devoted to sport and also high between all pairs of the five devoted to current affairs, but low between any sports programme and any current affairs programme. He displays the correlation coefficient in an array that clearly indicates this dichotomy without any more elaborate statistical analysis.

Exercise 18.5.   For the marks given in Table 8.5 (it may help you to take a copy [a photocopy if possible] of the table, p. 110, and work from that) calculate the correlation coefficients between (a) Chemistry and Physics, (b) Chemistry and French and (c) Physics and French. Interpret them in relation to your scatter plots of that data. A convenient way to display correlation coefficients is in a table like Table 18.4. In that table r_a, r_b, and r_c represent the coefficients you are to calculate and each refers to the coefficient between the two subjects named in the row and column labels.

Table 18.4.   *A correlation table*

	Chemistry	Physics	French
Chemistry	1		
Physics	r_a	1	
French	r_b	r_c	1

Time series

In Chapter 8 we referred to time series graphs, a subject with wide ramifications. Various techniques exist for extracting information from time series and for using them to make predictions. In Exercise 8.3, Table 8.6, we gave sales figures for raincoats. Not unexpectedly these showed a strong seasonal pattern. People are more likely to buy raincoats in autumn or early winter than in late spring or mid-summer. Seasonal effects are one manifestation of regular periodicity. Demand for electric power shows not only seasonal peaks and troughs but also shorter periodicities of a weekly and daily nature. Within a week less electricity is used at weekends (when there is less industrial demand) relative to weekdays. Within each day there are distinct morning and evening peaks and a pronounced trough between midnight and 6 a.m.

Unemployment figures show fluctuations during the year; superimposed on any trend there is a tendency for the level to be relatively higher in winter than in summer (when there are more 'seasonal' jobs available – in the tourist industry, agriculture, construction, etc.). In late summer school leavers unable to obtain jobs immediately may again increase unemployment totals. For this reason it is common to quote not only raw figures but seasonally adjusted figures, which allow for such differences without distorting long-term trends that may be present.

Thus a common interest in 'time series' data is to see whether there is any trend after allowing for periodic fluctuations and irregular 'hiccups'. *Time series analysis* is a major branch of statistical theory and practice, but even a simple graph of a time series often indicates major trends. These can often be clarified by simple techniques to smooth out irregularities or remove seasonal fluctuations. A detailed treatment is beyond our remit, but the interested reader is referred to Yeomans (1968, Chapter 6) or, at a more advanced level, to Chatfield (1980).

We consider only some simple data demonstrating rather clear trends.

Example 18.5. Table 18.5 gives data abstracted from the Scottish Development Department's *Statistical Bulletins*, 1984, prepared by the Government Statistical Service.

Table 18.5. *New dwellings completed in Scotland (hundreds)*

Quarter	First	Second	Third	Fourth
1981				
Private sector		29	28	27
Public sector		24	20	19
1982				
Private sector	25	31	29	29
Public sector	13	12	10	13
1983				
Private sector	30	33	32	
Public sector	10	11	12	

Figure 18.6 is a time series graph of this data. As is conventional in such graphs (though of debatable desirability) we have joined successive time points within each of the sectors – *public* and *private*. It is quite clear that during the period covered there is a sharp downward trend in public sector completions between the second quarters in 1981 and 1982, but then a levelling off. For the private sector there is a suggestion of a slight upward trend. There is also a hint of a 'seasonal effect' in the private sector in that completions peak in the second quarter of 1982 and 1983. Since we have no data for the first quarter of 1981 we cannot say whether there was also a peak in the second quarter of 1981. To be reasonably sure there is a genuine and continuing seasonal trend with peaks in the second quarter we would need data covering more years. However, it is well known that the private house buying market generally peaks in spring and early summer so it is perhaps not surprising that com-

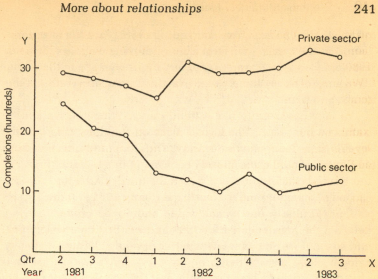

Figure 18.6. Time series for Scottish housing completions.

pletion of new homes is high at this time, no doubt intended to catch the summer buying market.

A general trend curve is often fitted to such data with the dual objective of smoothing out seasonal fluctuations and irregular data hiccups.

There are a number of methods of fitting trends. We discuss only a simple one.

Moving averages

We concentrate for a moment on the *private sector* figures in Table 18.5. If we take the average of four successive quarters we get an annual average per quarter. Thus if there is a seasonal effect this should be 'smoothed out'. For the first four data values – second quarter 1981 to first quarter 1982 – the mean is $(29 + 28 + 27 + 25)/4 = 27.25$. If we now drop the first value but introduce the value for the second quarter of 1982 we get an average $(28 + 27 + 25 + 31)/4 = 27.75$. Proceeding in this way – dropping off the first value each time and adding in its place the next observation in the series – we form a set of *moving averages*. The first moving average is an average of observations one to four, the second an average of observations two to five, the third of observations three to six, and so on.

We may use these to plot a *trend curve*. Where do we put the points on our graph? The logical place on the time scale is at the middle of the four points we average. Thus for points one, two, three and four it should come midway between points two and three. For our example that is midway between the third quarter for 1981 (our second observation) and the fourth quarter for 1981 (our third observation). Similarly our second value should be plotted midway between the fourth quarter for 1981 and the first quarter for 1982, and so on. If we do this we get a series of points. Joining them by a smooth curve gives a trend. Figure 18.7 shows trend lines constructed this way for both the public and private sector data of Table 18.5, together with the original time series as in Figure 18.6.

The trend lines show the steep decline in completions in the public sector over the first year, followed by a levelling off. In the two

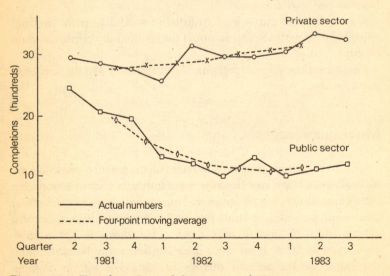

Figure 18.7. Trends in Scottish house completions.

fourth quarters (1981, 1982) covered by the data there is a suggestion that in the public sector completions rise above the trend. This suggests some seasonal pattern, but, as in the case of the private sector, one would need more data (for earlier or later years) to confirm this. Potential reasons for a peak at this time are less obvious than for a spring private sector peak, but it may be tied to budgetary considerations influencing the time of starting (thus indirectly of completion) of certain public sector building. This data itself is insufficient to confirm consistency with any such hypothesis; it merely suggests an interesting facet that may be worth exploring.

In the private sector the trend line suggests that the number of completions may be rising slowly over the period once allowance is made for seasonal and irregular fluctuations.

Some modified moving averages

Two criticisms can be made of the four-point moving average used above. They are: (i) we are forced into the artificial device of plotting smoothed points between observed points so we cannot claim to be smoothing specific observed points; and (ii) all four points used in each average are given equal weight. This means that a hiccup in a nearby point affects our value as much as a hiccup at a more remote point included in the average. Intuitively we may feel this is unfair if our moving average is designed to reflect local behaviour.

The first criticism could be overcome by taking a moving average of an odd rather than an even number of points. Thus if we take an average over five points this gives us a 'smoothed' value corresponding to the middle point of the five. However this approach has one serious disadvantage for quarterly data where there is a marked seasonal effect – the moving average is contaminated, or confounded, with the seasonal effect. If, for example, we take for the housing data a five-point average in the private sector, for the first five points we have two *second-quarter* (in 1981 and 1982) observations, but only one for each of the remaining quarters. The next moving average introduces two sets of third-quarter data and so on. While we may smooth out hiccups in this way we do not get rid of a seasonal effect.

By using a five-point moving average our second objection above is also reinforced, points even further away having as much influence as the value at the point at which we are attempting to get a smoothed value.

Both these objections (the first of which is only relevant with seasonal effects in quarterly or half-yearly data) may be overcome by using a weighted moving average. Instead of taking the straight mean of five consecutive points we take instead a weighted mean of these points, giving a weight of one to points one and five, and a weight of two to points two, three and four.

Thus in our housing example our first five points are observations on quarter two, 1981, with weight one; on each of quarters three and four, 1981, and quarter one, 1982, with weights two; and on quarter two of 1982 with weight one. Thus we have *one* observation on each of quarters three, four and one with weight *two*, but *two* observations (1981 and 1982) on quarter two each with weight *one*. In this way we balance out seasonal effects. For this particular data the final trend-line will not be very different from that obtained using the four-point unweighted moving average.

Exercise 18.6.   Using the weights just given, calculate five-point moving averages for the private sector data in Table 18.5. Plot the trend line and compare it with that already obtained for the four-point unweighted average. Obtain also five-point unweighted moving averages and plot them. State which trend line is most meaningful and why.

Note that if we use a five-point moving average the first point we plot corresponds to the third in our data set and the final point to the third observation from the end. Why can we not calculate our trend lines right to the end?

Trend curves can be created by other techniques than moving averages or by using moving averages with a variety of weighting systems and a larger run of points: e.g. seven points, nine points, eleven points, etc. Generally speaking, for data showing seasonal patterns a weighted five-point moving average, weights chosen as above, is adequate for quarterly data. For monthly data a weighted or even unweighted five-point average usually suffices as the seasonal effects are only repeated after every twelfth observation so there is no unbalancing of the seasonal effect. On the other hand, because the whole cycle of twelve months is not covered, seasonal effects are not removed; only hiccups (and sometimes short-term periodicities) are ironed out. A more elaborate technique is needed to produce seasonally adjusted data. See, for example, Yeomans (1968, Chapter 6).

5 Reports

19 Getting the act together

The target audience

Proper data presentation is a vital part of many technical or financial reports. To write a good report is not easy. Selfish writers produce documents more satisfying to themselves than to a reader; this is counter-productive. Two common aims in writing a report are (i) to provide information for others and/or (ii) to 'sell' our own ideas or suggestions. Before writing a report you should ask yourself: Why am I writing this? Who do I hope will read it?

There are several books on how to write good scientific and technical reports. *Effective Writing* by C. Turk and J. Kirkman (1982) is comprehensive. The authors draw attention to many pitfalls in presenting information. While our main concern is the presentation and interpretation of data, this aspect cannot be divorced from more general communication by words. Data, in tables or graphs, is an integral part of many reports, but unless it is blended with words it will not communicate effectively.

Poor style is a common weakness in technical writing. Do not confuse this with pedantry – split infinitives and prepositions at the end of a sentence should be avoided if possible, but they are only minor irritants. Sentences that are too long or ambiguous or incomprehensible, words used unnecessarily or carelessly, are hallmarks of bad style.

There is a widely held but erroneous belief among technical writers that use of long words or phrases – excess verbosity – adds to the stature of a report by making it in some way more 'scientific'.

Just as one can use too many words or the wrong ones, so too with data, one may use the wrong set or display it in an unsuitable way.

Blending words and numbers

Data in reports should be neatly dovetailed with verbal text, so first a few words about general problems of presenting technical material. How 'technical' a report should be depends upon the intended readership. If you are preparing a report on a new machine tool that your company hopes to sell to the motor industry you will probably want to provide both technical information for engineers and financial data for accountants. Jumbling the two together won't help sales!

You have two options: the first to write two reports, one for the engineers, one for the accountants. There will be some overlap, so if you reject this approach and opt for just one document it is essential to signpost it so that each type of reader can identify the parts of interest to him or her. Maybe you can divide it into several sections: an introductory section describing the equipment in broad terms, what tasks it can undertake and its advantages over existing machine tools. Avoid in this section as far as possible technical terms likely to be known *only* to engineers or *only* to accountants. The second section might be for engineers and deal with specifications and operating characteristics. Here you may use technical terms that would be understood by engineers – but avoid excess verbosity. The final section might be aimed at accountants; here standard financial jargon is acceptable, but again avoid verbosity. Neither engineers nor accountants care whether you know a lot of obscure words; using these will only detract from the clarity of what you are trying to say.

Layout

Lay out your report to make reading as easy as possible. Do not pile on information so rapidly that it cannot be digested; do not on the other hand be so detailed and slow that the report becomes a boring discussion of trivia; do not present facts in such a complicated way that the reader is tied in mental knots as he tries to disentangle them.

Make proper use of sentences and paragraphs. Ideally, present one fact per sentence and one theme per paragraph.

All this may seem obvious, but one often sees technical papers with sentences like this:

> As an initial working hypothesis we assume (subject to adjustment in the light of further information that may become available) that the production cost per unit for each of the two processes may for all practical purposes be regarded as identical.

For whatever audience he is writing the author would do better to say:

> Initially production costs per unit are assumed to be almost the same for each process. We shall drop this assumption if new information contradicts it.

Not only have we saved words. The message is clearer. With the first version some readers may be uncertain of the meaning of that word 'hypothesis', remembering only that it is a word used by mathematicians and scientists that has something to do with a belief or theory; they may be even more mystified by a *working* hypothesis; do some work better or harder than others? In the first version the reader's mind is distracted by the qualification in parenthesis, telling him we might or might not do something to a hypothesis that *at that stage* has not even been stated. The phrase 'for all practical purposes may be regarded as identical' is long-winded jargon for 'almost the same'.

In our second version not only is there a 40 per cent saving in words, but the logical order is sounder. Everyone likely to read a financial or technical report knows what an assumption is. We are told immediately what assumption is being made; then that we will alter it if new facts contradict it.

We are all guilty of using long-winded phrases when a simple word or two suffices. A prime example we hear almost daily on radio or TV is 'at this moment in time' for 'now' or 'at present'.

Improving readability

There is more to making text readable than changing words or using them more carefully and economically. Ordering of material is important, so is the layout of pages; use of spaces, indentations, sensible headings and sub-headings, careful numbering of sections and tables and illustrations, all help the reader. Too many reports are chronological accounts of what the author did, often cluttered with detail of little or no interest to the reader.

The right ordering of information depends on the purpose of the report. If it is commissioned by a manager wanting recommendations on how to do something, he will have asked you to provide them because you are the expert (or at any rate in his eyes the appropriate person for the job). In this case it might be best to start with your recommendations, then back them up with an account of the reasoning or evidence that led you to make them. Even this might be split into two sections, one a general discussion of how you weighed up the evidence; the other (perhaps relegated to an appendix) giving the evidence itself, often in the form of detailed graphs or tables. One warning: do not relegate to an appendix any tables or graphs that are an integral part of your argument. If you are quoting specific figures from a table have this as near as is practicable to where you quote those figures.

Whatever you do, leave out irrelevant material. The manager is unlikely to care a damn if the records were recorded manually until 3 July 1978 and thereafter automatically by computer *unless* this has some bearing on the accuracy and relevance of the data as a basis for making recommendations. If it has, then you must explain as briefly as possible the how and why.

Different formats

We have just described the appropriate layout for one type of report. If your report is not making recommendations for immediate action but is for the long-term record, a different format will be appropriate. For example, if the aim is to save unneeded repetition of research by letting others know you have already done it, the research might be described first and the conclusions given at the end.

If your report is written to encourage somebody to give you more money to develop a new piece of equipment, see that it shows the idea is practicable and highlights the economic advantages of that development. Financial backers are likely to be more generous if they can see a potentially good return for their investment.

Preparing a report

Suppose you are the production manager for a firm that markets a certain machine tool. Your boss is about to discuss with trade union representatives a bonus scheme for employees. He wants you to recommend a scheme.

Do not be surprised if at first he is vague about what he wants. He may not have thought very much about it. Pin him down. *To produce a good report you must know what is wanted*. Does he want you to make a detailed analysis of costs of competing bonus schemes? He may say 'no', and explain his broad ideas – perhaps that bonus payments should not exceed 10 per cent of basic salary, they should not be so attractive as to lead to over-production or forced redundancies. He may add, but perhaps only after some prompting from you, that he expects sales to increase by about 10 per cent next year. He may stress that he has to be ready to give a reasoned argument to trade union representatives as to why he is making specific proposals; he may also ask you to suggest counter-arguments if you believe some aspects of your proposals will be objected to by the unions, or to suggest where some flexibility might be introduced without damaging the basic scheme or making it too costly. He may want you to propose safeguards against abuses of the scheme.

However you go about producing it – whether by questioning, reading, or by experimenting – be clear about the objectives of your report before you start writing it, even before you collect basic information. It is not easy to pin down people on what they want in a report, or even why they want it. In the long run it saves everybody time if objectives are pinpointed at the start.

Look upon a report requisitioned by someone as a job you are doing for a customer. Be prepared to indulge his whims if these are harmless; it may save friction. If you think his ideas are plain crazy you must be able to justify your objections. As in most things, collaboration rather than confrontation usually produces the best results in report writing.

Collecting information

For the bonus scheme example we suppose a long discussion with your boss has made it pretty clear what is required. How do you set about the task?

It is unlikely all the information you need will be 'at your fingertips'. If, as is often the case in preparing a report, there are no existing tables or graphs with information you need, you will have to prepare these specially. Think carefully, bearing in mind some of the points in earlier chapters, how best to present information. Even if you take great care it is unlikely that your first 'working tables' will be in a suitable form for the final report. In preparing final tables or derived graphs, always bear your potential readers in mind. Are they likely to be good at interpreting figures, or would you be wise to spell out for them things that are obvious to you? Would they be happier with a graph than a table? Should there be both?

Your boss may have stressed that for his talks with union representatives he will want average production figures over the past three years, some idea of the pattern of monthly variation, also an indication of any trends in production, e.g. is it steadily increasing, or decreasing, or did it reach a peak from which it is now declining, or a trough from which it is now rising? He may also add that he attaches great importance to production rate per man employed.

To do your job you will have to turn up company records and in all likelihood do some elementary arithmetic to come up with the necessary figures. Your first draft of a table of production figures may look like Table 19.1.

You are not being very helpful to the boss if you just leave this on his table and expect him to work out trends and other characteristics. You will need more figures, e.g. numbers employed each month, to get rates of production per man employed. At this stage think if there

Table 19.1.   *Monthly production (units) 1981–83*

Month	1	2	3	4	5	6	7	8	9	10	11	12
1981	73	72	69	64	68	71	55	32	67	79	83	79
1982	74	77	78	75	81	84	54	29	73	82	91	93
1983	97	95	64	62	60	61	51	18	53	57	61	63

is relevant supplementary information, e.g. sales and profit figures, that may be useful. You should think at this stage whether a table or a graph best represents the data in Table 19.1.

Exercise 19.1.   Present the data in Table 19.1 as a time series graph.

Table 19.1 tells us a little about production trends. Your graph should convey similar information. Production always dips in July and falls even further in August. As production manager you immediately associate this with annual holidays, the plant always closing the last week in July to reopen mid-August. It is also easy to see that, ignoring those two months, the 1982 production is always higher than that for the corresponding month in 1981. Also, after a good start in 1983 production falls sharply in March, remaining depressed until the end of the year. As production manager you will know the change in March 1983 is associated with falling sales and that by the end of 1983 there was a reasonable production/sales balance with sales of about sixty units per month.

You may have to dig quite deeply into your firm's pay office records to get the number of production workers employed each month over the three-year period. Here there could be a problem about what to record when drawing up the analogue of Table 19.1. The numbers of employees at the beginning and end of any month will not always be the same – some may have left or extra hands may have been taken on. You must decide on a reasonable compromise. Possibilities include the mean or median daily number of employees for the month – or numbers employed at the middle of the month. The precise choice will make little difference if numbers remain reasonably steady, but the differences could be important if there were sudden changes in staffing levels. In practice this should be explored before deciding what to record.

Table 19.2.   *Mid-month employee totals 1981–83*

Month	1	2	3	4	5	6	7	8	9	10	11	12
1981	24	24	22	26	25	25	26	27	27	27	28	28
1982	28	28	30	31	32	32	33	30	29	34	34	34
1983	34	35	29	28	28	24	24	23	23	22	23	22

Table 19.2 gives numbers of employees at the middle of each month for the same three-year period as Table 19.1.

Exercise 19.2.   Present the data in Table 19.2 as a time series graph.

Using our tables

A quick glance at Table 19.2, or your graph, shows that apart from minor hiccups numbers employed tended to rise gradually during 1981 and 1982, but to fall after March 1983. We noted the sharp drop in production from March 1983 (Table 19.1) but there is a lag before the number of employees falls correspondingly. This slower decline might have been accounted for by a policy of allowing numbers to drop by natural wastage or voluntary redundancies rather than dismissals.

Tables 19.1 and 19.2 are useful starting points but they should be tidied up a little if they are to appear in a final report. One obvious improvement would be to replace the 1–12 labels for months by abbreviated names; Jan., Feb., Mar., etc. This may seem trivial but it is a worthwhile courtesy to the reader. Otherwise, if the report says something about the production drop in August the reader must recall that this is the eighth month of the year. Maybe you remember this automatically but most people take a moment or two to recall which is the fourth, seventh, eighth, etc., month. It might also help trend spotting to include row (yearly) averages and column (each given month) averages to help spotting trends and other forms of variation.

A derived table

Remembering that the boss is also interested in monthly production rates per man, we must derive these from Tables 19.1 and 19.2. We divide each entry in Table 19.1 by the corresponding entry in Table 19.2. The results are given in Table 19.3. Note we have given the figures to only one decimal place in accord with principles enunciated in Chapter 1 and emphasized throughout this book.

Table 19.3. *Monthly production per man 1981–83*

	Jan.	Feb.	Mar.	Apr.	May	Jun.	Jul.	Aug.	Sep.	Oct.	Nov.	Dec.
1981	3.0	3.0	3.1	2.5	2.7	2.8	2.1	1.2	2.5	2.9	3.0	2.8
1982	2.6	2.8	2.6	2.4	2.5	2.6	1.6	1.0	2.5	2.4	2.6	2.7
1983	2.9	2.7	2.2	2.2	2.1	2.5	2.1	0.8	2.3	2.6	2.7	2.9

This table indicates low production rates in July and August – attributable largely to the holiday period. Production rates are also relatively low in the spring and early summer of 1983 due to the lag in reducing numbers of employees to match lower output dictated by falling demand.

These tables, together with the knowledge gained from experience and discussions with the boss about what is required, are the basic raw material for recommendations that are to go into a report.

A decision still has to be made on what production level should qualify for a bonus. How should the bonus be distributed to encourage men to reach certain targets – and what should those targets be – without being so attractive that men are likely to be put out of work because of overproduction? The boss is unlikely to want this to happen – the unions certainly won't!

Decision time

It is obvious from Table 19.3 that monthly production rates of 3.0 and 3.1 per man can be achieved. The boss has asked you to research the bonus situation partly because he wants your expertise in telling him what are reasonable rates. If rates like 3.1 per month were achieved only by working considerable overtime the union will soon pick this up and would quickly contradict assertions that this is a reasonable rate under normal working conditions. If on the other hand you know that little or no overtime was worked in any 'high production rate' months, the argument for regarding them as reasonable is much stronger. To encourage men to reach a production rate of 3.0 it might seem fair to start making bonus payments only when production per man rises above 2.8 units. If you feel this to be so, it will be reflected in your final report. You will also have to take into account the projected 10 per cent increase in production and sales above that prevailing in the latter part of 1983. Will your bonus scheme allow for this without having to lay men off and without, one hopes, having to take on too many additional hands? If the unions felt the bonus scheme so attractive it could lead to overproduction and redundancies they may justifiably oppose it. On the other hand they will want it to give each of their members the best possible deal short of causing redundancies. It is on points like this your boss will face hard negotiation. You will help him if your report gives a reasonable analysis of how the scheme is expected to operate.

You may think of special features. Could production in the holiday months be increased by special bonuses in July and August? Points like this must be considered before writing your report. Your decision will be based on available data to back up your general 'know-how' about the business.

In the next chapter we give a suggested layout for your report based on the thinking we have outlined here.

20 *A specimen report*

The final version

We start this chapter with the final report prepared by the production manager, Mr Piggott, for his boss Mr Hogg for the bonus scheme example in the last chapter. This is produced in facsimile form on the following pages. At the conclusion we discuss the salient features.

A critique of the report

The report is fairly typical of a well laid out and reasonably well composed document that might be produced in a company for internal use. We now examine it under several headings pointing out strengths and weaknesses.

1 General layout

Layout not only helps readability, but the ease with which a report can later be referenced or referred to in a discussion – especially at meetings or over the telephone. That is why the pages (other than the title page) are all numbered. Note, too, it is divided into three sections, and paragraphs or main sub-sections within each section are numbered by a decimal system. If Mr Hogg wants to discuss a point on the phone with Mr Piggott and each has a copy in front of him it is helpful to be able to say 'On page 2, paragraph 3.3 in the fifth line you say "If production is 69 units . . ." '

Similarly if, at a committee meeting where all participants have a copy, Mr Hogg wants to refer to section 1.3 on page 1 he has just to say so and everyone soon finds the right spot.

There are a lot of possible numbering systems for sections and

RECOMMENDATIONS FOR AN EMPLOYEE BONUS SCHEME

Prepared for Mr G.V.Hogg by

P.Piggott

22 February 1984

Summary

Production records for 1981-83 indicate that a monthly production
rate of 2.8 or more units per employee is reasonable. With 23
employees a target production rate of 69 units per month would
require a production rate of 3.0 units per month. Past records
indicate this target is attainable and seems reasonable with
bonus incentives. A bonus of 1 per cent on basic earnings is
proposed for each 0.02 units by which the rate exceeds 2.8 with
a maximum bonus of 10 per cent in any month for a production rate
of 3.0 or higher. Special provisions are suggested for bonuses
during holiday periods. If the full bonus is regularly earned
production targets should be achieved with 23 employees, one
more than at present.

1. RECOMMENDATIONS

1.1 In each month except July and August the company should offer to each employee a bonus calculated as follows:

> If the average monthly rate of production exceeds 2.8 units per employee a bonus of 1 per cent of gross wages (excluding overtime) will be paid for every 0.02 units by which the average exceeds 2.8, subject to a maximum of 10 per cent if the average is 3.0 or higher.

1.2 In the month of July the company should offer to each employee a bonus calculated as follows:

> If the average monthly rate of production exceeds 2.2 units per employee a bonus of 1 per cent of gross wages (excluding overtime) will be paid for every 0.02 units by which the average exceeds 2.2, subject to a maximum of 10 per cent if the average is 2.4 or higher.

1.3 In the month of August the company should offer to each employee a bonus calculated as follows:

> If the average monthly rate of production exceeds 1.4 units per employee a bonus of 1 per cent of gross wages (excluding overtime) will be paid for every 0.02 units by which the average exceeds 1.4, subject to a maximum of 10 per cent if the average is 1.6 or higher.

1.4 No bonus shall be payable in any month to an employee who is in the Company's employ for less than 3 full weeks in that month, nor to an employee who is absent from work for reasons other than illness for a period exceeding 7 working days in that month.

2. AIM OF RECOMMENDATIONS

2.1 The recommendations aim to achieve an approximate 10 per cent increase on current production rates. If production rates guaranteeing maximum bonuses are achieved only one additional employee will be needed to reach targets.

2.2 If, as anticipated, our market share increases by only 10 per cent the recommended scheme with its bonus cut off when production rate exceeds 3.0 (other than in July/August) should discourage production exceeding our target, thus avoiding a need for lay-offs or redundancies unless our sales forecasts prove over-optimistic.

2.3 The special schemes for July/August are designed to boost production in these months. Records for the past three years given in Table 1 indicate consistently low production due to annual holiday closure.

NOTE: Average rates of 2.2, 1.4 for triggering bonus payments
in July, August respectively, exceed the rates achieved
for these months in 1981-1983. It is possible the Union
representatives will press for a lower trigger for bonuses
in these months. If so, it should be pointed out that
the Company is making a concession in offering a bonus
on reduced production in these months as any extra payments
will also be included in holiday pay which covers a 'non-
productive' period.

3.   BASIS OF RECOMMENDATIONS

3.1 A study of

     (i) total output,
     (ii) workers employed,
     (iii) average monthly output per worker

     suggests that the targets and triggers for bonus payments
     given in section 1 of this report are reasonable. A summary
     of these statistics for the years 1981 to 1983 is given
     in table 1 overleaf.

3.2 Important features of the table relevant to my
     recommendations are:

     (i) the fall-off in production from March 1983 to the
     end of that year;

     (ii) excluding July/August each year (holiday period)
     and March, April, May 1983 (when obviously workforce not
     fully stretched due to decreased production) the average
     number of units produced per worker remains reasonably
     steady between about 2.6 and 3.0;

     (iii) the fall-off in production rate during July/August
     is not unexpected, but even after allowance for plant
     closure of approximately one week in July and two in August
     production at this time of year is disappointing.

3.3 On the basis of recent production matching sales (with
     an average sales figure of 59.2 units per month from March
     to December 1983) it seems reasonable to aim for an average
     production of some 65/66 units per month in 1984 to meet
     an expected 10 per cent increase in sales. If production
     is 69 units in each of the ten non-holiday months, 55
     units in July and 35 units in August the total for the
     year would be 780 units with an average of 65 per month.
     To produce 69 units per full month with 23 employees implies
     a production rate of 3.0 units per employee. This rate
     was achieved in the first quarter of 1981 with no more
     than normal levels of overtime. The production superintendent
     regards a rate of 2.8 as acceptable but considers that
     a rate of 3.0 is a reasonable target that would not put
     undue pressure on workers.

TABLE 1

Monthly production (a), Numbers of employees (b) and
Production per employee (c), 1981-83

Month	Jan	Feb	Mar	Apr	May	Jun	Jul	Aug	Sep	Oct	Nov	Dec	Average
1981													
(a) Prod	73	72	69	64	68	71	55	32	67	79	83	79	67.7
(b) Emp	24	24	22	26	25	25	26	27	27	27	28	28	25.8
(c) P/E		3.0	3.1	3.1	2.5	2.7	2.8	2.1	1.2	2.5	2.9	3.0	2.8
1982													
(a) Prod	74	77	78	75	81	84	54	29	73	82	91	93	74.2
(b) Emp	28	28	30	31	32	32	33	30	29	34	34	34	31.3
(c) P/E		2.6	2.8	2.6	2.4	2.5	2.6	1.6	1.0	2.5	2.4	2.6	2.7
1983													
(a) Prod	97	95	64	62	60	61	51	18	53	57	61	63	61.8
(b) Emp	34	35	29	28	28	24	24	23	23	22	23	22	26.2
(c) P/E		2.9	2.7	2.2	2.2	2.1	2.5	2.1	0.8	2.3	2.6	2.7	2.9
Monthly averages* 1981-83													
(a) Prod	81	81	70	67	70	72	53	26	64	73	78	78	67.8
(b) Emp	29	29	27	28	28	27	28	27	26	28	28	28	27.8

*to nearest whole number

3.4 The above considerations explain the recommendation of 2.8
as a 'norm' to trigger bonuses. It could be embarrassing if
the production rate regularly exceeded 3.0 per month as
lay-offs might then be necessary. Further, in view of
the company's good industrial relations record we would
not wish to encourage a production rate that placed undue
strain on employees. For these reasons I recommend a maximum
bonus of 10 per cent when a rate of 3.0 or higher is attained.
The simplest scheme is to pay the bonus pro rata on any
excess of production over 2.8 but not exceeding 3.0, i.e. at
the rate of 1 per cent for each 0.02 excess over 2.8. The
bonuses payable would then be:

Av. production	2.82	2.84	2.86	2.88	2.90	2.92	2.94	2.96	2.98	3.00
Bonus per cent	1	2	3	4	5	6	7	8	9	10

No additional bonus would be payable for a production
rate exceeding 3.0 per man per month.

3.5 The holiday months of July-August present a special problem.
We should encourage higher production at this time. Since
only the last week (sometimes not a complete week) of July is
in the holiday period a production drop of some 20 per cent
seems reasonable. This suggests the threshold rate for a
bonus should be about 80 per cent of 2.8 (i.e. approximately

2.24). For administrative simplicity I recommend in section
1.2 a rate of 2.2 to trigger off bonuses in July. Since
there is no production during the first two weeks in August
it seems reasonable to expect half the normal production
rate in that month, so I recommend in section 1.3 a rate
of 1.4 to trigger bonus payments in August.

3.6 In the note at the end of section 2.3 it is suggested
that the Union representatives may consider these trigger
points high as they exceed the rates actually achieved
in 1981-83 during July and August. I think we should argue
for these trigger points along the lines indicated in
that note. However, if there are strong pressures to lower
these figures some ground could be given here with less
effect upon production or costs than a similar relaxation
in general trigger levels, since the latter operate for
ten months in each year.

3.7 Our standard provisos re employees not working a full
month are included in paragraph 1.4. You may recall we
had some misunderstanding with the Unions several years
ago through failing to specify a condition of this type.
As with our previous bonus schemes, I recommend excluding
overtime payments from the calculations.

3.8 It is not clear when agreement with the Unions might be
reached and the scheme implemented. If there are serious
delays in negotiations a careful watch should be kept
on production and sales trends and it might be wise to
reserve the right to withdraw the bonus offer if agreement
cannot be reached in a reasonable time.

paragraphs. Some official government reports have paragraphs numbered consecutively from beginning to end. I prefer a decimal system within sections, but it is advisable not to have too many subdivisions. In our specimen report we use only two – the first giving the section and the second the paragraph or sub-section within that section. If sub-sections are further divided, references like 6.3.5 are appropriate to refer to the fifth paragraph in the third sub-section of section six. Don't carry this too far – a reference to 7.6.16.2.9 won't be easy to find!

Avoid complex mixtures of numbers, upper and lower case letters, Roman numerals. References to 5 (A) xii (q) are not easy to pick up. We are all fairly good at ordering Arabic numerals, but less good at quickly deciding whether xvi is larger or smaller than xiv or whether (q) comes before or after (o) – not to mention confusion between the letter 'o' and the number '0'! It is however quite in order to use Roman numerals (or letters) for sub-clauses as in section 3.1 and 3.2 if these are few in number.

In the report considerable use is made of indentation; used discriminatingly this is a valuable aid to reading. If Mr Hogg wants to spot quickly the key recommendations they are indented on page 1 in sections 1.1–1.3.

Note, too, the ordering of the contents. The recommendations come first. Mr Hogg asked for recommendations, so let him see them straight away. They might make his blood boil – if they do he will read on to see why Mr Piggott is coming up with such foolish suggestions. Then again, if he has confidence in Mr Piggott's judgement and likes his suggestions he may feel he only needs to skim through the rest of the report!

It is true, of course, that Mr Piggott did a lot of thinking and pored long over data before making those recommendations – but he spares Mr Hogg the details – hard grind is what he is paid to do. He puts recommendations first, then back-up. Section 2 gives reasons leading to the advice while section 3 gives background information, essentially the material Mr Piggott used as a basis for his thinking on what would be appropriate. Mr Hogg (depending on his degree of interest in figures) may not look at Table 1 in detail, but it presents material that should be there. It might be needed in negotiations if they run into difficulties.

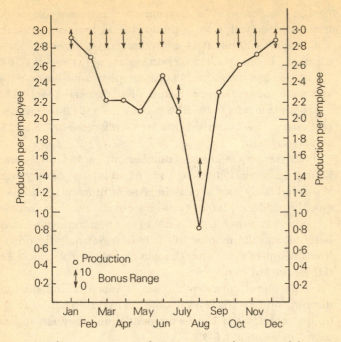

Figure 20.1. Production per employee 1983 and proposed bonus levels.

What about graphs or diagrams? There are none in the report. There is a strong case for at least one graph like that in Figure 20.1. This shows for 1983 the actual production per employee and how it measures up to bonus start and bonus peak levels.

We see that had the system operated that year, bonuses would have been paid in January and December while in February, July and November production was close to the bonus trigger. Mr Hogg and Mr Piggott know that a sales slump in the spring of 1983 while the workforce was being only slowly reduced accounts for the low production rate from March to June. The graph could be used to show union negotiators at a glance that the targets are not unrealistic. Using colours, a slide of this graph could be made for an overhead projector – a useful tool during discussions. In many reports graphs will be useful – if they are prepared carefully. Avoid graphs like

Figure 9.1. Do you think you could improve on Figure 20.1? What about similar graphs for 1981 and 1982? Think whether your readers are likely to prefer graphs or tables.

So much for general layout. What about specific matters?

2   The title page

A good title page is important. The boss will probably have a lot of papers on his desk. He wants to be able to identify each quickly. The format may be beyond your control; there may be company rules on how you lay this out. The firm may have a supply of paper printed with the company name and space allocated for title, author, circulation list and perhaps a summary. If so, one must learn to live with it; we have assumed no such inhibition. The important thing is the title. Make it relevant. Position it to stand out; in CAPITALS, underlined or in bold type. One-third to one-half of the way down the page is eye catching – with plenty of blank space above and not too much crowding below. The company will want their name on it somewhere, and if they want a filing reference that too must be provided. There will almost certainly be company policy on where this information should appear – it's sensible to have this in the same place for all documents. Top left (as here) or bottom of the title page are favourite spots for this sort of information together with indications of confidentiality, etc.

Circulation lists, if needed (none for our document), are best at the bottom left (or perhaps top right) of a title page.

Unless there are very good reasons for remaining anonymous, the author's name should appear not too far from the title with other information if relevant (position, qualifications, etc.). We assume Hogg knows who Piggott is.

If the date is required it can be given close to the title/author information, as here; alternatively top or bottom right are good places for this.

A summary on the title page is an option. Do not put it there if it is going to crowd the page. If it does it is probably too long (except in the case of a very long and complex report).

3　The summary

For a report likely to be read by only a few people for a very specific purpose (as in our example) a summary is perhaps a luxury. Mr Hogg called for the report; it is mainly for his eyes; he knows what it is about, or should be about, but nevertheless it might be handy for him to be able to see the general gist of the report.

To be of any use a summary must be informative. The following summary would be virtually useless:

> This report suggests a minimum production rate at which bonuses might be paid and a scale of bonuses for various production rates for normal working months and those in which the plant is closed for holidays. Reasons for the recommendations are given.

This is all true – it is what Hogg asked Piggott to do, but it does not tell us what Piggott *has* done. The summary on our title page gives Hogg a good idea of what he will find in the report. From it he learns immediately that production rates between 2.8 and 3.0 are going to earn a bonus, he knows in broad terms how it is to be spread over the range and that the maximum will be 10 per cent. He is alerted about special provisions for holidays (which might be something he had not thought about before). He sees that he needs about twenty-three employees to meet targets if the scheme works.

4　Numerical information

This aspect is of special concern to readers of this book. Is Table 1 a good table? The answer is a qualified yes. It condenses the information in Tables 19.1, 19.2 and 19.3 into one table and gives further figures in the form of various row and column averages. We can look easily at the figures for each month in each year and note the trends or peculiarities mentioned in the report.

It is handy to have production figures and numbers of employees one above the other for each month. Thus if 'P/E' is low for a particular month we can glance above and see if this was because the total production was low or if for some reason the number of employees was especially high. In nearly all cases where the rate is low it is because production is down. The number of employees fluctuates less markedly from month to month than does total output.

The annual averages in the final column simply provide a yard-stick to see whether the corresponding observation for any one month in that year is above or below average.

The horizontal lines breaking data by years are an aid in reading, as is the gap between the 'number of employees' line and the 'P/E' value. This draws our attention to the fact that the latter is derived (by taking the quotient) from the relevant entries in the two lines above the gap.

There are two weaknesses in the table. It is doubtful whether the monthly averages for 1981–83 given in the last segment of the table for production and employees are much use. They highlight the production drop for July–August – but that is obvious from the fig-ures for each year separately. Mr Piggott might well have left them out. The second weakness is that if you want to pick out, say, the P/E ratio for April 1983 it needs extra care to pick up the correct entry because it is a long way from the month name at the top of the table to the row corresponding to 1983 P/Es.

This latter difficulty could be overcome in one of two ways – by using vertical rules to separate columns – not too difficult on a typewritten document (even if only done by hand on the master before duplicating or photocopying) but unpopular for printing, unless very modern methods are being used. A better solution is to repeat month names within each year just above the 'Production' rows, rather than just having them once at the top of the page. The only problem about this is that it gives the table a rather cluttered appearance and in a sense introduces redundant information.

There is one other table in the report. Unnumbered, it is the two-line table in section 3.4. It is a short table that reads as part of the text in that section and is not referred to elsewhere. When a short table forms part of continuous text it is permissible (indeed advis-able) to incorporate it without displaying or numbering it separately unless you want to refer to it from elsewhere in the text.

5 Clarity

In Chapter 19 we warned that long words and wrong words, unclear sentences and excess verbosity are common faults in technical reports. How does our example measure up on these pitfalls? Not too badly, I think, but see if you agree.

Exercise 20.1.   Work through Mr Piggott's report and see if you can make any worthwhile improvements in wording. Some can be made, but probably most will be minor. For example, the recommendations on page 1 require careful reading, but I think their intention is clear.

In some technical reports you might see section 1.1 replaced by something like this. It means the same.

1.1 For each month other than the months specified in sections 1.2 and 1.3 hereunder a bonus calculated as follows shall be payable:
    (i) the average production rate in that month expressed as the number of items produced divided by the number of employees in employment on the fifteenth of that month shall be calculated.
    (ii) If the average calculated in (i) above has a value of or less than 2.8 the bonus shall be zero.
    (iii) If the average calculated in (i) above has a value of or in excess of 3.0 a bonus of 10 per cent shall be payable.
    (iv) If the average calculated in (i) above falls between the maximum value specified in (ii) above and the minimum value specified in (iii) above the bonus payable shall be calculated at the rate of 1 per cent for each multiple of 0.02 by which the said average exceeds the maximum specified in (ii) subject to that calculated bonus not exceeding 10 per cent.
    (v) in calculating any bonus the percentage shall be a percentage of gross salary excluding any overtime payments.

Phraseology like that above (with a little more care in drafting) might be needed in drawing up a final agreement with the unions, but it is quite out of place in a technical report intended to suggest a basis for negotiation.

Note that finally the report deals with points that might be raised by the unions and makes suggestions where there might be flexibility (see, e.g., section 3.6). In sections 3.7 and 3.8 practical points concerning negotiations are raised.

One final piece of self-criticism. The report does not make clear what bonus would be paid for a production of, say, 2.83 units per month. Would it be 1 or 1.5 per cent? In other words it is not clear whether the bonus jumps in 1 per cent steps at 2.82, 2.84, etc., or increases continuously from 0 to 10 through the 'pro-rata' indicators set out in section 3.4 of the report.

Exercise 20.2. If you have access to any technical reports and know why they were written and for whom they were intended (especially any you yourself may have written) study them critically. How do they stand up to some of the criticisms of technical reports made above?

Exercise 20.3. Which of the following statements, A or B, do you prefer, and why?

A. The editorial board particularly desires to attract general expository articles on topics of current importance to the statistical community. Such articles should be styled for our general readership and should be authoritative and well researched. Authors with plans for possible expository papers are urged to communicate with the Editor with an outline or draft of the proposed article.

(Publication policy statement, *The American Statistician*)

B. The editorial board welcomes authoritative, well-researched, expository articles on topics currently important to statisticians. The style should be suitable for our general readership. Authors planning such papers are advised to send the Editor an outline or draft.

Can you produce a version giving the same information but better than either A or B? If you think you can, get a friend (or, even better, an enemy) to cast a critical eye over your version and give an opinion.

Exercise 20.4. Which of the following, A or B, would make you more enthusiastic about subscribing or contributing to a new journal, assuming the subject matter were relevant to your work?

A. The Journal will provide a common medium for the dissemination of significant information in all branches of statistical planning and related inference problems. By statistical planning is meant any work concerned with the collection of data either from experiments or investigations and whether it is collected in one or several attempts. Thus the scope will be wide-ranging and will encompass problems of handling and transmission of data and information. Papers which discuss important applied problems, papers containing significant theoretical results and those combining theory and applications will be included.

(From an advertisement for a new statistical journal)

B. The Journal will publish informative papers on statistical planning and inference. Statistical planning covers data collection from one or more experiments or investigations, including problems of handling and transmitting data and information. Papers discussing important applied problems, containing significant theoretical results, or covering both theory and application, will be published.

Has anything of importance from version A been omitted in version B?

Exercise 20.5. Self-criticism is good for the soul. Here is an extract from Sprent (1981, p. 207):
'Table 70 gives the marks for the same 10 students in French, German and Mathematics.

Table 70   *Students' marks in three subjects*

	A	B	C	D	E	F	G	H	I	J
French	83	27	42	51	53	44	47	55	61	33
German	74	22	49	54	48	47	55	61	59	29
Mathematics	64	11	66	65	59	52	50	91	83	55

'A glance at Table 70 shows that student B is bottom of the class in all three subjects, while student J, who is second from the bottom in the two languages, has performed rather better in Mathematics. There are also differences in the mark allocations in the three subjects; in French the marks range from 27 to 83, in German from 22 to 74 and in Mathematics from 11 to 91.'

I could have been more helpful in my presentation. How?

6 Addenda

21 Lifeboat

In this chapter we give hints and solutions to exercises which were not followed in the text by a detailed discussion, or which are so open-ended that a discussion here is inappropriate as it would be too wide-ranging.

Exercise 1.3, p. 17 Tape reader gives intermittent trouble from 20 May onwards, especially 23, 26 May. Graph plotter has no particularly bad spell.

Exercise 1.4, p. 21 Shortest one second, longest fifty-five seconds. No obvious patterns of the types suggested. This contrasts sharply with some later data (Table 17.3, p. 224).

Exercise 2.1, p. 26 Three wins would give Southampton 79 points so they could be champions, but note goal difference inferior to Liverpool and Manchester United. No other team can win.

Exercise 2.2, p. 26 Wolves and Notts County certain to be relegated as neither can attain 47 points. Other possible relegation candidates are WBA, Sunderland, Ipswich and Norwich, although if any of the remaining fixtures include a match between any of the teams on 47 or 48 points, those on 49 or 50 points are safe.

Exercise 2.3, p. 27 Arsenal (same number), Luton.

Exercise 2.4, p. 30 Absolute increase for Technology is 121.5 − 85 = 36.5. No other difference exceeds 21.5.

Exercise 2.5, p. 31 £1000 would purchase 2439.02 Australian units at 41p. Many Trusts calculate number of units allocated to two decimal places.

£500 purchases 1037.34 units at 48.2p. If sold at 60.4p these raise £626.55, thus profit is £126.55. If sold at 56.4p, profit would be £85.06.

Exercise 3.1, p. 37 18 out of 90, giving 20 per cent.

Exercise 3.2, p. 40 A suitable stem and leaf display is given in Table 21.1.

Table 21.1.   *Stem and leaf display of car prices*

Stem	Leaf								
20 *	00								
24	00	50	95						
25	00								
26									
27	00	00	25	45	50	50	75		
28	50	50	75	75	95				
29	00	00	00	45	50	50	95	95	99
30	00								
31	00	00	00	25	25	50	75	75	99	99
32	50	50							
33	00	95							
34	50								
35	00								

Features include preponderance of 'leaves' (tens and unit digits) with values 00, 25, 50, 75 suggesting a tendency to ask prices rounded to £25. Bunching of prices on '29' stem may indicate a psychological ploy to emphasize this price is still in the £2000-plus range and not in the £3000-plus range. Prices concentrated on '31' stem may imply a desire by these sellers to obtain a price of at least £3000 even after some bargaining.

Exercise 3.3, p. 40 Stem and leaf may not be appropriate for small data sets or if data ranges widely with little concentration on any subsection of scale, or if data are counts which show little variation.

Exercise 3.4, p. 43 Histogram might use intervals based on stems in Table 21.1 and would then look like that stem and leaf display tipped on its side.

Exercise 4.3, p. 50 Table could be presented in several ways. One possibility is to replace the numbers in Table 4.3 by actual breakdown times. The first three lines of the new table would now appear as in Table 21.2.

Table 21.2. *Daily distribution and times of printer failures*

Day	Duration (minutes)						
	0–9	10–19	20–29	30–39	40–49	100–109	140–149
1					49		
4	7		21, 24				
5		11, 19					

Exercise 4.4, p. 50 As CPU failures are fewer in number than printer failures your tables will be sparser in entries, but this is offset by a greater spread of breakdown times for the CPU.

Exercise 4.5, p. 53 A diagram like Figure 21.1 is suitable.

Exercise 4.6, p. 53 Your frequency table should look like Table 21.3. Tally marks would be omitted from the final version.

Suggestion of more breakdowns during day than there are in evening. In Table 1.2 it is apparent that strings of minor breakdowns often occur within an hour on one day; e.g. printer breaks down five times between 1400 and 1500 on 13 May.

Exercise 5.3, p. 61 The downward trend for vehicles under 1000 cc. is a little easier to spot in the new table as it is not lost in the clutter of detail. See comments on p. 19 re mental ability to assess and manipulate two-digit numbers.

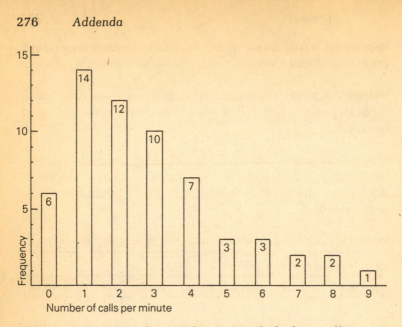

Figure 21.1. Frequency diagram for receipt of telephone calls.

Table 21.3.   *Distribution of breakdown times throughout working day*

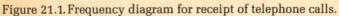

Time		Number of breakdowns
0800–0859	╫╫ ‖‖	9
0900–0959	╫╫ ╫╫ ‖	11
1000–1059	╫╫ ‖‖	9
1100–1159	‖‖	3
1200–1259	╫╫ ‖‖‖	9
1300–1359	╫╫	5
1400–1459	╫╫ ╫╫	10
1500–1559	╫╫ ‖‖	9
1600–1659		0
1700–1759	╫╫ ‖‖	8
1800–1859	‖‖	3
1900–1959	╫╫ ‖‖	7
2000–2059	‖	2
2100–2159	‖‖	3
2200–2259	‖	2
2300–2359		0
	Total	90

Exercise 5.4, p. 63 Due to round-off some totals are 99 or 101, but this is no cause for alarm.

Exercise 5.5, p. 67

Table 21.4. *Agricultural workers*
(thousands), classified by
employment category and sex

	Male	Female	Total
Full time	499	52	551
Part time	99	95	194
Seasonal	168	126	294
Total	766	273	1039

Column totals agree with row totals in Table 5.9 and row totals agree with row totals in Table 5.8.

Exercise 5.6, p. 67 Marked decrease between 1977 and 1983 in full-time employees of both sexes (Tables 5.7 and 5.8). A less pronounced decrease in part-time employees. Numbers of seasonal employees of both sexes remain steady. The proportion of full-time female workers is only about one-tenth, whereas there are approximately the same numbers of part-time workers of either sex and about 60 per cent of seasonal workers are males.

Exercise 6.1, p. 74

Five-number summary is (3, 8, 11, 22, 51) indicating positive skewness and long tail to right.

Table 21.5. *Stem and leaf display for magnesium content*
(second stage)

Stem	Leaf														Total
0	3	4	5	6	6	7	7	8	8	8	8	9	9	9	14
1	1	1	3	5	8	8									6
2	0	1	2	3	4										5
3	1	1	9												3
4	1														1
5	1														1
														Total	30

Exercise 6.2, p. 74   Suitable stems are 'clusters' of five successive digits, 0–4, 5–9, etc. Leaves are unit digits on each stem. The 'Stage 2' display is given in Table 21.6.

Table 21.6.   *Stem and leaf display of traffic intervals*

Stem	Leaf
0–4	1 1 1 1 1 1 2 2 2 2 2 2 2 3 3 3 3 3 3 3 3 3 3 4 4 4 4 4 4 4 4
5–9	5 5 5 5 6 6 6 6 6 6 6 7 7 7 7 7 7 8 8 8 8 8 8 9 9 9
10–14	0 0 0 0 0 0 1 1 1 1 2 2 3 3 4 4 4 4 4 4
15–19	6 6 6 7 7 7 8 8
20–24	2 2 3 3 3
25–29	5 5 6 9
30–34	1 4
35–39	6
40–44	3
45–49	7
50–54	
55–59	5

Stem and leaf display indicates positive skewness with long tail to right.

Exercise 6.4, p. 80   Mean 10.2; standard deviation 5.84.

Exercise 6.5, p. 80   Batting averages are obtained by dividing total score by numbers of *completed* innings. In effect a 'not out' score is added to the next innings, or to the previous completed innings if a batsman is not out in his final innings.

Exercise 6.6, p. 80   Median of £8275 is preferable. Mean is strongly influenced by extreme income of £124 742, for the only family earning more than the mean income.

Exercise 6.7, p. 81   The numbers are too large for many pocket calculators to handle. Even if your calculator does floating-point arithmetic (which effectively means expressing numbers like 27 543 817 421 as 2.7543817421 10 (the ten indicating the decimal point is to be shifted ten places right) there is still likely to be a rounding error. My calculator uses floating-point arithmetic, but for the second data set it gives a negative sum of squares of deviations from the mean! One way around this problem is described in Appendix A. From there we see that our calculations of standard deviations are not altered if we subtract the same number from all observations. Try the calculations after subtracting 17 431 000 from all observations in the first set. For the second set try subtracting 17 432 191 from all observations.

Exercise 7.2, p. 83   In general layout your diagram should resemble Figure 21.1.

Exercise 7.3, p. 86   Summary of calculations:
For Table 1.1, sum of squares of all observations = 543 156.
Sum of observations is 4042 and number of observations 90, whence variance is 4018.06 and standard deviation 63.39.

For Table 7.2, total sum of squares is

$$4.5^2 \times 24 + 14.5^2 \times 22 + \ldots + 334.5^2 \times 1 = 547\ 792.5.$$

Sum of all observations is 4035, whence variance is 4076.56 and standard deviation 63.85.

The difference is due to the fact that in the second case all data is assumed to be at the middle of the group.

Exercise 7.5, p. 91   (a) since 160 is 213% of thirty-year average, average is

$$160 \times \frac{100}{213} = 75 \text{ (to nearest integer)}.$$

(b) 595.
(c) thirty-year average for Edgbaston 776, Newcastle 640.

Exercise 8.1, p. 96   Sydney 35%, Melbourne 30%, Brisbane 15%, Adelaide 12%, Perth 5%, Hobart 3%. These give proportions for pie chart and relative heights for bar diagram.

Exercise 8.2, p. 110   Your scatter diagrams should clearly indicate that for Physics and Chemistry most points lie reasonably close to a straight line passing through the mark points corresponding to a total of 20 in each subject and to a total of 80 in each subject. For either of the sciences and French there is a much broader scatter of points. Thus, given a candidate's mark in Physics, say, it is easy to predict roughly the mark he might get in Chemistry, but difficult to predict his score in French.

Exercise 8.3, p. 111   Sales show marked seasonal pattern with large drop in summer. In 1985 and first half of 1986 Wetshield have appreciably higher sales, especially in winter. Damp-off sales show strong rise to overtake their rivals in latter half of 1986. Total market for the two firms in corresponding months of each year shows minor fluctuations but no marked pattern of differences between years.

Exercise 9.1, p. 113   For mineral products expenditure drops shar- from 1980 to 1982 but recovers to 1980 level by 1984. Vehicles show a similar trend but recovery is not so complete. Electrical engin- eering expenditure rises slightly from 1980 to 1982 and sharply from 1982 to 1984. In each year expenditure on mineral products is less than that in the other sectors. Vehicle expenditure leads other sec- tors in 1980, 1982, but is overtaken by electrical engineering in 1984.

Exercise 9.2, p. 116   No cause for alarm. Small discrepancies due to rounding to nearest integer.

Exercise 9.3, p. 116   Whether you prefer graphs or tables is largely a matter of personal choice. Graphs often have the edge when general pattern is of more interest than detail.

Exercise 9.4, p. 121   The box plots are shown in Figure 21.2.
Groups B and C show sharp drop in numbers compared to control. Group D shows a modest drop and group A a small drop. Groups B

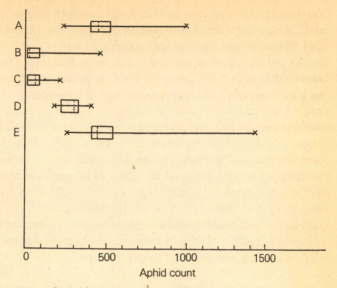

Figure 21.2. Box plots of insect counts on beans.

and C probably treated with the only really effective insecticides. Little to choose between these. The lower median for B is attractive, but so is the lower upper quartile and lower greatest value for C. The relative positions of the boxes is of most interest.

Exercise 10.1, p. 129 Using method indicated in text, within limits dictated by graph (i) 58 m.p.h., (ii) 53 m.p.h., (iii) 54 m.p.h. For greater accuracy one should use published timetable and official table of distances for calculations of average speeds.

Exercise 10.2, p. 133 Three stops, first at number 32 (two readings between 8.4 and 8.6), second at number 35 (below 8.4), third at number 39 (above 9.6).

Exercise 10.3, p. 137 Program reads five numbers into the computer, determines their sum and product and prints these out.

Exercise 10.4, p. 140 Invest in Number Nine inflation-proof gilts.

Exercise 11.2, p. 148   Multiply area by density to get population of each State or territory. Add to get total population. Divide by total area. This effectively is obtaining weighted mean of densities, using area as weights. Average density is 1.92. Note that if we simply add all densities and divide by 8, the number of States and territories, we get a mean of 15.68. Explain why this is misleading!

Exercise 11.3, p. 149   APRs are 12.7, 16.1, 19.6, 23.1, 34.5, 42.6.

Exercise 11.4, p. 150   At 9.3 per cent per annum ($= 9.3/12 = 0.775$ per cent per month), credited monthly, £1.00 grows in one month to £1.00775. Thus in 12 months it grows to £$(1.00775)^{12} = $ £1.09707, equivalent to an APR of 9.71 to two decimal places.

At 9.2 per cent credited daily similar arguments show £1.00 grows to £$1.00025205^{365} = $ £1.09635 in one year, equivalent to an APR of 9.64, thus first investment is marginally better.

Exercise 11.5, p. 152   APRs are 67.8, 180, 1164, 14 104.

Exercise 11.6, p. 154   0.0404. (Cancellations between numerator and denominator (something we bother to do less in the age of the pocket calculator) give an exact fractional value of 4/99.)

Exercise 11.7, p. 155   The answer you should get is 1 exactly. When I fed the numbers straight into my pocket calculator I got 0.871649355! One way to avoid our 'rounding' problem here is to note that we should get the same answer if we divide the first number by 1 000 000 000, giving 1.743298710, and multiply the second number by this same factor to get 0.5736251592. The product of these may come to exactly one, or something near to it, depending on the number of digits your pocket calculator holds in its register. Even if we round to four decimal places we find

$$1.7433 \times 0.5736 = 0.99995688.$$

Exercise 12.6, p. 163   The five-number summaries are:

Mathematics (20, 41.5, 51.5, 57.5, 81)
English (23, 43, 51, 60, 79)

Note the similarity between these summaries. That for English differs little from the summary for the 'raw' marks. That for Mathematics shows how extreme marks have been drawn towards the centre.

Exercise 13.2, p. 170

$$I = \frac{(0.5/20) \times 20 + (220/250) \times 92}{(0.5/20) \times 17 + (220/250) \times 46} = 199.1.$$

Exercise 13.3, p. 173 For 1962–84 the greatest relative change is in transport, the weighting increasing by a factor of 2.32. Between 1973 and 1982 the largest relative increase is in services, which increase by a factor of 1.22 (durables increase by a factor of 1.19).

Exercise 13.4, p. 179 Goods costing £1 in 1968 would cost £4.04 in 1980. Goods costing £1 in 1980 could have been purchased for 32p in 1972. I would have to pay £5.39 in 1984 for goods costing £1 in 1968.

Exercise 15.3, p. 194 The thirty-six samples of seven are formed by omitting all possible pairs of two pages from the nine. The paired pages omitted can be written down in a convenient order of page numbers as

(1,2), (1,3), (1,4), (1,5), (1,6), (1,7), (1,8), (1,9), (2,3), (2,4), (2,5), (2,6), (2,7), (2,8), (2,9), (3,4), (3,5), (3,6), (3,7), (3,8), (3,9), (4,5), (4,6), (4,7), (4,8), (4,9), (5,6), (5,7), (5,8), (5,9), (6,7), (6,8), (6,9), (7,8), (7,9), (8,9)

Check carefully that we have listed all pairs of pages to be omitted.

Exercise 15.5, p. 195 To get the mean of all samples of seven accurately work with sample totals rather than means (these suffering rounding on division by seven). The total for all thirty-six samples of 7 must be divided by $36 \times 7 = 252$ to get the mean of all sample means since each sample total is seven times its own sample mean.

Exercise 15.6, p. 201 Some addresses may be of houses that do not include a defined household, or they may be unoccupied or have been demolished since the register of addresses was compiled.

Exercise 17.1, p. 219   For each of heads *and* tails

(observed − expected)^2/expected = $6^2/20$ = 1.8.

Adding for heads and tails gives a test statistic of 3.6, which is less than the value of 3.84 which would indicate evidence the coin were biased. Thus we accept the hypothesis that the coin is fair. With thirteen heads and twenty-seven tails the statistic becomes

$$2 \times 7^2/20 = 4.9.$$

Since this exceeds 3.84 we conclude there is sufficient evidence to conclude the coin might well be biased.

Exercise 17.3, p. 221   The test statistic has the value 6.4, much less than the value of 16.92 required for significance.

Exercise 17.5, p. 223   Digits odd and even alternating.

Exercise 17.6, p. 223   Reject hypothesis of uniform distribution of breakdowns as value of statistic is approximately thirty-two, i.e. appreciably greater than twenty-five.

Exercise 17.7, p. 225   Total 471. Sum of squares 7359. For 100 observations mean is 4.71 and standard deviation 7.17.

Exercise 18.4, p. 236

$$r = \frac{-100}{\sqrt{(1042.86 \times 550)}} = -0.132$$

Exercise 18.5, p. 238   The following will help your calculations of correlation coefficients:

Chemistry: Total 1313, sum of squares 87115.
Physics: Total 1192, sum of squares 72180.
French: Total 1177, sum of squares 68213.
Chemistry and Physics: sum of products 78962.

Chemistry and French: sum of products 71839.
Correlation coefficients:
Chemistry and Physics: 0.959
Chemistry and French: 0.235

We leave you to work out that between Physics and French without further prompts.

Exercise 18.6, p. 244 Moving average values are:

Quarter	81/4	82/1	82/2	82/3	82/4	83/1
five-point weighted	27.50	27.87	28.25	29.12	30.00	30.63
five-point unweighted	28	28	28.2	28.8	30.4	30.6

Unweighted moving average is less informative. Since first and fifth value both contain two second-quarter (high) values these get pushed up relative to preceding value and despite trend are close to following values with only one second-quarter reading. Overall effect is to mask the upward trend evident with the weighted moving average.

Exercise 20.5, p. 270 To make comparisons easier I should have ordered candidates in decreasing order of merit in one subject, say French. This would make order of candidates A, I, H, E, D, G, F, C, J, B.

Appendix A: coding data

Shifting the origin

If numbers are represented by points on a straight line the zero point is called the origin. If we *subtract* the same constant a from all the numbers we say the origin has been shifted to a. For example, if our numbers are 1, 3, 5, 6.2, 8.1 and we subtract 5 from all observations they become -4, -2, 0, 1.2, 3.1, i.e. our original number 5 now becomes zero; that is, the origin has been shifted to the point 5. It is intuitively obvious – and quite easy to demonstrate algebraically – that if we shift the origin in this way then the mean of the observations undergoes the same shift.

The original data 1, 3, 5, 6.2, 8.1 has mean 4.66 (verify this). When we shift the origin to 5 we get, as above, the numbers -4, -2, 0, 1.2, 3.1 with mean -0.34. We easily verify that $4.66 - 5 = -0.34$.

Changing the scale

If we multiply each of a set of numbers by a constant, b, say, we change the scale, i.e. expand (or contract) the distances between points representing numbers. We call b a scale factor. This scale factor affects the mean the same way, i.e. it is also multiplied by b. We saw above that the mean of our original set of five observations was 4.66. If we multiply each by 3 we get 3, 9, 15, 18.6, 24.3. You should verify that the mean of these rescaled numbers is 13.98 and that $4.66 \times 3 = 13.98$.

Since subtraction of a number a is equivalent to addition of $-a$ and multiplication by b is equivalent to division by $1/b$ we easily establish the rules:

1. If we add or subtract the same constant to/from all data, the

mean of the new data is obtained by adding or subtracting the same constant to/from the mean of the original data;

2. If we multiply or divide all data by the same constant factor the mean of the new data is obtained by multiplying or dividing the mean of the original data set by the same constant.

This device is useful if we are dealing with large numbers that may lead to overflow or excessive rounding with a pocket calculator. More generally it may be used to save work when entering numbers on to a pocket calculator keyboard if the leading digits of all of them are comparable.

Example. Suppose we require the mean of the following numbers:

17 432.4, 17 432.6, 17 432.8, 17 432.9, 17 433.1.

Clearly if we subtract 17 432.0 from all of these we get the simpler set 0.4, 0.6, 0.8, 0.9, 1.1. If we find decimal points a bit of a nuisance we could now multiply these each by 10, obtaining 4, 6, 8, 9, 11. It is a mental arithmetic exercise (but take a pocket calculator if you do not trust your mental powers) to see that the sum of these numbers is 38, and hence the mean is 38/5 = 7.6. To get the mean of the original data we reverse the process of *subtracting* 17 432 and then *multiplying* by 10; i.e. we first *divide* by 10, then *add* 17 432. Thus the mean of our original data is (7.6/10) + 17 432 = 0.76 + 17 432 = 17 432.76.

We might use the dodge of subtracting 3000 if we had records of heights of all mountains in England and Wales over 3000 feet and wanted to find their mean height.

Variance and scale and origin changes

Since variance is a measure based on deviations from a mean it is fairly easily established that a change of origin, i.e. adding or subtracting the same constant from all observations, *does not alter the variance* – this follows since the *same* change in each observation implies the same change in the mean.

However, multiplication of all observations by a constant b does affect the variance; the variance of the new data is b^2 multiplied by the variance of the original data. Taking the data set 4, 5, 8, 11 we easily see that the mean is 7 and the variance 7.5 (check this). If we subtract 7 from all observations it is again easily verified that the mean is 0 and the variance still 7.5.

If, however, we multiply each of the original observations by 5 we get a new data set 20, 25, 40, 55 with mean now 35. You should verify by direct calculation that the variance is now 187.5, which is 25 (i.e. 5^2) times the original variance of 7.5.

Since the standard deviation is the positive square root of the variance (and the square root of b^2 is b) the effect of multiplying all data values by a constant is to multiply the standard deviation by the same constant. For the above data set, taking the square roots of the variances before and after transformation, i.e. of 7.5 and 187.5, we get the values 2.74 and 13.69, the latter being 5 times the former (allowing for a rounding effect in the second decimal place).

The advent of pocket calculators makes arithmetic much easier and change of origin and scale to 'save arithmetic' is less important than it was two decades ago. Nevertheless it is a useful device if there are dangers of floating point overflow or if it saves a lot of punching of leading digits all of which are the same, as in numbers like 7 432 193, 7 432 184, 7 432 982, 7 432 453.

'Chopping off' leading digits like the 7432 in this example saves some danger of errors in entering data on the keyboard of a pocket calculator (or into a computer) but the more important aspect is avoidance of rounding errors which easily occur in the calculation of variance.

The source of difficulty here is that the sum of squares of observations is often a large number; so too is the square of the sum divided by the number of observations, which we subtract from it in calculating a variance. The difference between these two is often small and greatly influenced by rounding in the two large numbers in the subtraction.

In practice it has been found that many computer programs run into difficulties with this type of calculation as it is hard to program a computer to do its own scaling sensibly. In Appendix B we give an alternative way of calculating means and variances which, although inappropriate for most pocket calculator applications, is ideal for computer programming.

As an example of coding to save arithmetic consider the data in Table 7.2. Suppose we subtract 4.5 from each interval mid-point and divide the result by 10. The 'coded' mid-point values become 0, 1, 2, 3, 4, 5, 8, 10, 12, 14, 17, 18, 23, 24, 33, i.e. the original tens digit (preceded by any hundreds digit) of the stem and leaf display in Table 3.3. For the coded values the mean is

$$\frac{0 \times 24 + 1 \times 22 + 2 \times 13 + \ldots + 33 \times 1}{90} = \frac{363}{90} = 4.033.$$

To get the mean of the original data we carry out the reverse transformation, i.e. multiply the mean by 10 and add 4.5, i.e.

$$10 \times 4.033 + 4.5 = 44.83,$$

the same result as we got on p. 84.

Appendix B: recursive formulae

Step-by-step means

If we have a set of r observations let us denote the mean by m_r. If we now obtain one additional observation, which we shall call the $(r + 1)$th observation, there is a convenient mathematical formula that says that the mean of all $r + 1$ observations, which we shall denote by m_{r+1} is given by the formula

$$m_{r+1} = m_r + \frac{d_{r+1}}{r+1} \tag{1}$$

where d_{r+1} is the value obtained by subtracting m_r from the additional observation.

Example. Suppose we have the observations 1, 3, 8, then clearly $r = 3$ and the mean $m_3 = 4$. Suppose now we are given an additional observation with value 10. Using the above formula we have $r = 3$, $d_4 = 10 - 4 = 6$, whence $m_4 = 4 + 6/4 = 5.5$. It is easily verified directly that this is the mean of the four observations 1, 3, 8, 10.

In practice one would be likely to use this formula with a pocket calculator only if one had calculated the mean of a data set and then found an additional observation one wanted to include.

However, with a computer program, problems with rounding can be reduced with this formula if it is used instead of the familiar form, $m_r = $ (sum of observations)/(number of observations), for the sum of large numbers is a larger number that could be subject to rounding error.

The formula (1) above is known to mathematicians as a recursive formula. We may use it first to calculate the mean of two observations given the mean of one (which is obviously the number itself!) and the value of the other. Having thus got the mean of two observations, then given a third we apply the formula again to get the mean of all three, then given the mean of all three and a further observation we apply it again to get the mean of all four (as we did in our example), and so we proceed for any number, n, of observations. The advantage of this method is that we work with numbers which are only of the same order of magnitude as our original observations, calculating what might be called a *running mean* but never computing totals of all observations.

Recursive sums of squares of deviations

However, it must be admitted that rounding problems with *means* are not common. As already emphasized, and demonstrated in Exercise 6.7, problems do occur in calculating variances. The source of the problem has already been mentioned in Appendix A. We may avoid it without the necessity of changes in origin or scale by using a recursive formula for sums of squares of deviations from the mean. Denoting the sum of squares of deviations of r observations from their mean by S_r the recursive formula relating S_r, to S_{r+1}, the corresponding sum of squares for $r + 1$ observations when deviations are taken from the mean of all $r + 1$ observations is

$$S_{r+1} = S_r + \frac{r.d_{r+1}^2}{r+1} \tag{2}$$

Formula (2) can be used for recursive calculations in parallel with formula (1). At each stage we need a value for S_r and d_{r+1} before we can calculate S_{r+1}. We can only calculate d_{r+1} after we calculate m_r.

For starting values we *always* take m_1 equal to our first observation (the mean of one observation is the value of the observation itself) and $S_1 = 0$. This latter is correct because the mean of the first observation is the value of the observation, so its deviation from its mean, i.e. itself, is zero and hence so also the square of that deviation.

In summary then,

$$d_{r+1} = \text{new reading} - \text{running mean}$$
$$= (r+1)\text{th reading} - m_r,$$

$$m_{r+1} = m_r + \frac{d_{r+1}}{r+1}$$

$$S_{r+1} = S_r + \frac{r.d_{r+1}^2}{r+1}$$

m_1 = first reading. $S_1 = 0$.

What is d_1?

Example. Consider the data set 1, 3, 5, 11. Since $m_1 = 1$ and $S_1 = 0$ we immediately calculate d_2 = second observation $- m_1$ $= 3 - 1 = 2$. Substituting in formula (1) gives $m_2 = 2$ and in formula (2) gives $S_2 = 2$. It is easily verified directly since $m_2 = 2$ that the sum of squares of deviations of observations 1 and 3 from that mean is $1^2 + 1^2 = 2$. We next calculate d_3 = third observation $- m_2$ as $5 - 2 = 3$, whence setting $r = 2$ in (1) and (2) leads to $m_3 = 3$, $S_3 = 8$, results easily verified directly for the observed values 1, 3, 5. The procedure is carried through once more with $r = 3$ introducing the new observation 11, giving finally $m_4 = 5$, $S_4 = 56$. The variance of the four observations is obtained by dividing S_4 by 4, the number of observations. Carry through these calculations yourself and make sure you can follow the steps just outlined.

This trivial example does not show the full power of the method in reducing rounding errors. However, it is worth noting that most operations are done on numbers lying between 1 and 11, the data range. Indeed in general only numbers in the data range (and n if it exceeds any data value) and the square of *one* of these occur in the calculations. We avoid numbers of the order of the sum of squares of the data.

Exercise. Find X, Y and Z to complete the following tableau:

Data: 6, 8, 4.

r	d_r	m_r	S_r
1	X	6	0
2	2	Y	2
3	−3	6	Z

Did you have trouble finding X? It does not matter what value we give it. We never use d_1!

Try this method on troublesome Exercise 6.7.

Appendix C: the sigma notation

Algebra and addition

This being essentially a book about numbers we have kept algebraic notation to a minimum. In your further reading you will almost certainly meet some algebra. It is a convenient mathematical shorthand.

One thing you will find if you read statistics books is the *sigma notation*.

Suppose we wish to write down formulae for mean and variance applicable to *any* set of observations. If n (which may be any positive integer) is the number of observations we may express *any* set of n observations as $x_1, x_2, x_3, \ldots x_r \ldots, x_n$ where x_r is simply the rth observation in the set and r may take any value between 1 and n. The sigma notation uses the Greek letter Σ to indicate the instruction 'take the sum'. If we want the sum of all our xs (call this S) we write

$$S = \sum_{r=1}^{n} x_r.$$

The r = 1 beneath the Σ tells us we are to take the sum of the x_r starting with x_1 and the n above says we are to finish with x_n.

i.e. $\sum_{r=1}^{n} x_r$ is shorthand for $x_1 + x_2 + \ldots + x_n$.

If it is obvious or implicit from the formula over what terms we are summing (in the above case all the n observations) we usually leave out the r = 1 below and the n above the Σ.

Using this notation the expression for the mean *m* of the above observations may be written:

$$m = (\Sigma\, x_r)/n = S/n.$$

Recalling the way we defined variance (p. 79) verify that the formula for calculating a sum of squares of deviations from the mean for n observations may be written:

(sum of squares of observations) $-\dfrac{\text{(sum of observations)}^2}{\text{number of observations}}$

In Chapter 18, page 230, we denoted this by S_x. In sigma notation we may write

$$S_x = \Sigma\, (x_r{}^2) - \frac{(\Sigma\, x_r)^2}{n}$$

Similarly the sum of products of deviations of corresponding x and y values from their mean (denoted by P on page 230) may, if we write a typical paired observation $(x_r,\, y_r)$, be written in sigma notation as

$$P = \Sigma(x_r y_r) - \frac{(\Sigma x_r)(\Sigma y_r)}{n}$$

Some people find the sigma notation rather awe-inspiring. If one remembers it simply means 'take the sum of all numbers of the kind represented by the symbol following it' the mystery disappears and it is really a very handy notation. Do not be put off by it in statistics books. It saves an awful lot of writing.

References

Some sources of data

Facts in Focus, Fifth edition (1980), London: Central Statistical Office: Penguin Books.

Monthly Digest of Statistics (includes an annual supplement *Definitions and Explanatory Notes*), London: Central Statistical Office; Her Majesty's Stationery Office.

Monthly Weather Reports, London: Meteorological Office; Her Majesty's Stationery Office.

Social Trends (annual), London: Central Statistical Office; Her Majesty's Stationery Office.

There are numerous collections of official statistics published by the statistical service of nearly every national government as well as international bodies such as the UN and the EEC.

Books

(E = elementary, C = comprehensive but parts not requiring specialist statistical knowledge, S = specialist, assuming some knowledge of statistics.)

Chatfield, C. (1980), *The Analysis of Time Series: An Introduction*, Second edition, London: Chapman and Hall (S).

Cochran, W. G. (1977), *Sampling Techniques*, Third edition, New York: John Wiley and Sons (S).

Cox, D. R. (1958), *Planning of Experiments*, New York: John Wiley and Sons (E/C).

Davies, O. L. (ed.) (1956), *Design and Analysis of Industrial Experiments*, London: Oliver and Boyd (C).

Ehrenberg, A. S. C. (1983), *A Primer in Data Reduction*, Chichester: John Wiley and Sons (E/C).

Erickson, B. H. and Nosanchuk, T. A. (1979), *Understanding Data*, Milton Keynes: Open University Press (E/C).

Moore, P. G. (1980), *Reason by Numbers*, London: Penguin Books (E/C).

Pearce, S. C. (1983), *The Agricultural Field Experiment*, Chichester: John Wiley and Sons (C/S).

Pocock, S. J. (1983), *Clinical Trials: A Practical Approach*, Chichester: John Wiley and Sons (C/S).

Rowntree, D. (1981), *Statistics Without Tears*, London: Penguin Books (E).

Sprent, P. (1977), *Statistics in Action*, London: Penguin Books (E).

Sprent, P. (1981), *Quick Statistics; An Introduction to Nonparametric Methods*, London: Penguin Books (C).

Tufte, E. R. (1983), *The Visual Display of Quantitative Information*, Cheshire, Connecticut: Graphic Press (E/C).

Tukey, J. W. (1977), *Exploratory Data Analysis*, Reading, Massachusetts: Addison-Wesley Publishing Company (C/S).

Turk, C. and Kirkman, J. (1982), *Effective Writing*, London: E & F. N. Spon (E/C).

Wetherill, G. B. (1977), *Sampling Inspection and Quality Control*, London: Science Paperbacks (S).

Yates, F. (1981), *Sampling Methods for Censuses and Surveys*, Fourth edition, London: Griffin (C).

Yeomans, K. A. (1968), *Introducing Statistics: Statistics for the Social Scientist*, Vol. I, London: Penguin Books (C).

Index

FOR THE BEST IN PAPERBACKS, LOOK FOR THE 🐧

In every corner of the world, on every subject under the sun, Penguin represents quality and variety – the very best in publishing today.

For complete information about books available from Penguin – including Pelicans, Puffins, Peregrines and Penguin Classics – and how to order them, write to us at the appropriate address below. Please note that for copyright reasons the selection of books varies from country to country.

In the United Kingdom: For a complete list of books available from Penguin in the U.K., please write to *Dept E.P., Penguin Books Ltd, Harmondsworth, Middlesex, UB7 0DA*

In the United States: For a complete list of books available from Penguin in the U.S., please write to *Dept BA, Penguin, 299 Murray Hill Parkway, East Rutherford, New Jersey 07073*

In Canada: For a complete list of books available from Penguin in Canada, please write to *Penguin Books Canada Ltd, 2801 John Street, Markham, Ontario L3R 1B4*

In Australia: For a complete list of books available from Penguin in Australia, please write to the *Marketing Department, Penguin Books Australia Ltd, P.O. Box 257, Ringwood, Victoria 3134*

In New Zealand: For a complete list of books available from Penguin in New Zealand, please write to the *Marketing Department, Penguin Books (NZ) Ltd, Private Bag, Takapuna, Auckland 9*

In India: For a complete list of books available from Penguin, please write to *Penguin Overseas Ltd, 706 Eros Apartments, 56 Nehru Place, New Delhi, 110019*

In Holland: For a complete list of books available from Penguin in Holland, please write to *Penguin Books Nederland B.V., Postbus 195, NL-1380AD Weesp, Netherlands*

In Germany: For a complete list of books available from Penguin, please write to *Penguin Books Ltd, Friedrichstrasse 10 – 12, D–6000 Frankfurt Main 1, Federal Republic of Germany*

In Spain: For a complete list of books available from Penguin in Spain, please write to *Longman Penguin España, Calle San Nicolas 15, E–28013 Madrid, Spain*

A CHOICE OF PENGUINS AND PELICANS

Metamagical Themas   Douglas R. Hofstadter

A new mind-bending bestseller by the author of *Gödel, Escher, Bach*.

The Body   Anthony Smith

A completely updated edition of the well-known book by the author of *The Mind*. The clear and comprehensive text deals with everything from sex to the skeleton, sleep to the senses.

Why Big Fierce Animals are Rare   Paul Colinvaux

'A vivid picture of how the natural world works' – *Nature*

How to Lie with Statistics   Darrell Huff

A classic introduction to the ways statistics can be used to prove *anything*, the book is both informative and 'wildly funny' – *Evening News*

The Penguin Dictionary of Computers   Anthony Chandor and others

An invaluable glossary of over 300 words, from 'aberration' to 'zoom' by way of 'crippled lead-frog tests' and 'output bus drivers'.

The Cosmic Code   Heinz R. Pagels

Tracing the historical development of quantum physics, the author describes the baffling and seemingly lawless world of leptons, hadrons, gluons and quarks and provides a lucid and exciting guide for the layman to the world of infinitesimal particles.